Collins

Big book of
Crosswords

Published by Collins
An imprint of HarperCollins Publishers
Westerhill Road
Bishopbriggs
Glasgow G64 2QT

www.harpercollins.co.uk

HarperCollins*Publishers*
Macken House, 39/40 Mayor Street Upper
Dublin 1, D01 C9W8, Ireland

12

© HarperCollins Publishers 2016

ISBN 978-0-00-822094-5

Layout by Puzzler Media

Printed and bound in the UK using 100% renewable electricity at CPI Group (UK) Ltd

If you would like to comment on any aspect of this book, please contact us at the
given address or online.
E-mail: puzzles@harpercollins.co.uk

f facebook.com/collinsdictionary
🐦 @collinsdict

PUZZLES

Puzzle 1

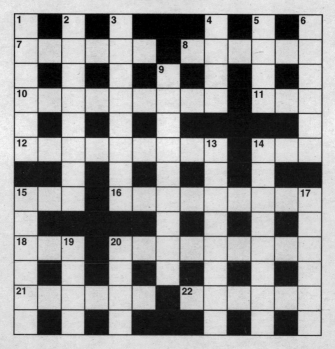

ACROSS

7 Canvas covering (6)
8 Mauled (6)
10 Money kept for bribes (5,4)
11 ___ de vie, brandy (3)
12 Cold whisked beverage (4-5)
14 Feline (3)
15 Sprout (3)
16 Sailing society (5,4)
18 Gullible person (3)
20 Inflatable part of a tyre (5,4)
21 Add, append (6)
22 Cause, bring about (6)

DOWN

1 Medicinal ointment (6)
2 Straightened (hair) (8)
3 Furtively (2,3,3)
4 Oaf (4)
5 Affectedly cute (4)
6 Alter (6)
9 Sweet tropical crop (5,4)
13 Install (a bishop) (8)
14 Mathematical system (8)
15 Lament (6)
17 Ale producer (6)
19 Obtains (4)
20 Linear measure (4)

Puzzle 2

ACROSS

1 Attach a description to (5)
4 Open (a jar) (7)
8 Accursed, damnable (7)
9 Buzzing noise of a machine (5)
10 Young blokes (4)
11 Finale (3)
12 Mistaken belief (4)
15 Shouting (6)
16 Small canine (3,3)
19 Partakes of (4)
21 Suitable (3)
22 Nibble, bite (4)
26 S American dance (5)
27 Entreat (7)
28 Detaching (7)
29 Backbiting (5)

DOWN

1 Written defamation (5)
2 Mildly (7)
3 Unwilling (4)
4 Not carried out (6)
5 Stitched (4)
6 Wet (weather) (5)
7 Wild pig with large tusks (7)
13 Crawling insect (3)
14 Sing with closed lips (3)
15 Stop being so sad! (5,2)
17 Go for a meal (4,3)
18 Observing furtively (6)
20 Chronological device (5)
23 Puny (5)
24 Car for hire (4)
25 Heroic tale (4)

Puzzle 3

ACROSS

1 Cockerel bred for eating (5)
4 Odious (7)
8 Delete (4,3)
9 Hooded anorak (5)
10 Twitchy (4)
11 Great pleasure (3)
12 Hindu mystic (4)
15 Huggable (6)
16 Plastic ducts or piping (6)
19 Strong cord (4)
21 Obtain for money (3)
22 Quick look (4)
26 Musical drama (5)
27 Lions etc when hunted (3,4)
28 Hallway above stairs (7)
29 Cope (3,2)

DOWN

1 Thick wire (5)
2 Forked (7)
3 Midday (4)
4 Milliner's packing (6)
5 Apexes (4)
6 Give up (5)
7 Going (7)
13 Sandwich filling (inits) (3)
14 Shed (3)
15 Share lifts to work (3-4)
17 Lacking accuracy (7)
18 Nonsense (6)
20 Clean feathers (5)
23 Holiness (5)
24 Hindu gown (4)
25 Dead keen (4)

Puzzle 4

ACROSS

1 Freshened (11)
9 Defiant person (5)
10 Warehouse workers (7)
11 Museum official (7)
12 'Go in' sign (5)
13 Types of earring (5)
15 Country lane (5)
20 Signify (5)
22 Berry-like fruit (7)
24 Small axe (7)
25 Forward (money) (5)
26 Sinister humour? (5,6)

DOWN

2 Trade blockade (7)
3 Dark (5)
4 Virtuoso (6)
5 Bow and arrow sport (7)
6 Incident (5)
7 Gap, chink (5)
8 Seize without authority (5)
14 Clairvoyant, medium (7)
16 Feeling embarrassed (7)
17 Brief and profound (5)
18 North polar region (6)
19 Malicious ill-will (5)
21 Part of a flower (5)
23 Inoculation fluid (5)

Puzzle 5

ACROSS

1 Luxurious, upmarket (4-3)
5 Border, rim (4)
10 Door for a pet (3,4)
11 Pop group's CD (5)
12 Righteous (5)
13 Have as a consequence (6)
15 Cut out (6)
17 Be more partial to (6)
19 Flesh of a nut (6)
20 Pay (5)
23 Currents (5)
24 To and from (7)
25 Skin opening (4)
26 Constricting snakes (7)

DOWN

2 Entomb (5)
3 Extreme vulnerability (12)
4 Person's sibling's son (6)
6 Report on a mission (7)
7 'Dutch disease' trees (4)
8 Scuttle (7)
9 Central electrical control (6,6)
14 Existing (7)
16 Somerset gorge (7)
18 Without muscle (6)
21 Colour of envy (5)
22 Halt (4)

Puzzle 6

ACROSS

1 Phrase differently (6)
4 Luxuriate (in) (6)
9 Bracketed (7)
10 Vital organ (5)
11 ___ and ends, scraps (4)
12 Go back in (2-5)
14 Anxious, troubled (6)
16 Discussion (6)
19 Drawing (7)
21 Froth (4)
23 Very coldly (5)
24 Fail (of a company) (2,5)
25 Guarantee (6)
26 Sparsely (6)

DOWN

1 Large stone (4)
2 Posing as (5-2)
3 Baps (5)
5 Reach, attain (7)
6 Lowest amount (5)
7 Liquid-filled mattress (8)
8 Garnish (5)
13 Large motorcycle (4,4)
15 Atomiser (7)
17 Desert (7)
18 Public persona (5)
20 Long operatic solos (5)
21 Pull the chain? (5)
22 Become worn at the edges (4)

Puzzle 7

ACROSS

1 Tittle-tattle (6)
5 Plant disease (6)
8 Marvellous! (4,4)
9 Cry of woe (4)
10 Inscribe with acid (4)
11 Wildly excited or active (8)
12 Pencil sketch (4,7)
15 Moment of firing (8)
18 Allay (4)
20 Shock (4)
21 Over the moon (8)
22 Soul (6)
23 Any non-acid (6)

DOWN

2 Unconcealed (5)
3 Tell me to stop pouring! (3,4)
4 Checked (7)
5 Move, stir (5)
6 Furious (5)
7 Domestic warmth (7)
12 Illuminate (5,2)
13 Inability to remember (7)
14 First-aid accessory (3,4)
16 More central (5)
17 Chemically unreactive (5)
19 Drop (liquid) (5)

Puzzle 8

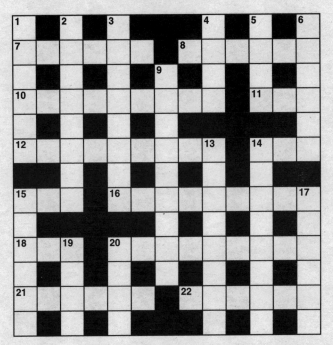

ACROSS

7 Without a friend (6)
8 Craving food (6)
10 Spiny marine creature (3,6)
11 Posed (for a picture) (3)
12 Become definite (4,5)
14 Rowing boat pilot (3)
15 Jotter (3)
16 Differently (9)
18 Hardwood (3)
20 Speak ill of (9)
21 Sign on as a soldier (6)
22 Last part (6)

DOWN

1 Cupboard (6)
2 Plain (police car) (8)
3 In the open air (8)
4 Scottish brook (4)
5 A long time (4)
6 Sentence structure (6)
9 Giving a hiding to (9)
13 Maddening (8)
14 Of the weather (8)
15 Tried and tested (6)
17 Dynamism (6)
19 Curly cabbage? (4)
20 Amount of medicine (4)

Puzzle 9

ACROSS

1 Personal journals (7)
5 Steady engine sound (4)
10 Impromptu (2-3)
11 Freeze up (3,4)
12 Music celebrity (3,4)
14 Close to (4)
16 Curl up (6)
18 Vivid shade of blue (6)
20 Work-shy (4)
21 Uttered, declaimed (7)
24 Reclaim (3,4)
25 Nautical berth (5)
27 Terminates (4)
28 Detailed location (7)

DOWN

2 Badly, wrongly (3)
3 Disprove (5)
4 Political exile (6)
6 Attempt, try (4,1,4)
7 Blood-stained (4)
8 Deadening (sound) (7)
9 Abutting shed (4-2)
13 Wrote a later time on (4-5)
15 College pupil (7)
17 Elbow-room (6)
19 Preserved, cured (6)
22 Internal sore (5)
23 Cast amorous glances at (4)
26 Mode of road transport (3)

Puzzle 10

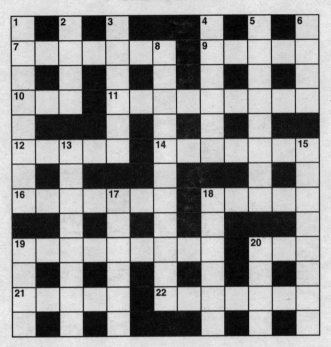

ACROSS

7 Pop star's followers (3,4)
9 Employ once more (5)
10 Psychic power (inits) (3)
11 Seafood item (4,5)
12 Fatigued (5)
14 Noting (7)
16 Phrasing, enunciation (7)
18 Fold in cloth (5)
19 Hypermetropia (4,5)
20 Hive insect (3)
21 Stories (5)
22 Invalidate (7)

DOWN

1 Had an influence on (8)
2 Real bargain (4)
3 Came away in scales (6)
4 Real, decent (6)
5 Flee in horror (3,1,4)
6 Slant, tilt (4)
8 Financial worker (4,7)
13 Of late (8)
15 Prepare (3,5)
17 Demand emphatically (6)
18 Soil fertiliser (6)
19 Many (4)
20 Seethe (4)

Puzzle 11

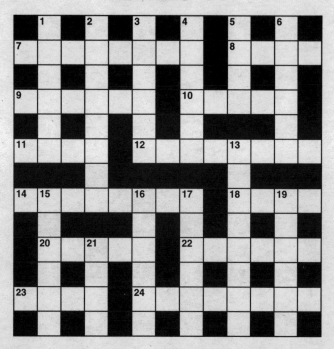

ACROSS

7 Drinks coolers (3,5)
8 Carry (4)
9 French-style café (6)
10 Rustic scene (5)
11 Opposed to (4)
12 Produce, give rise to (8)
14 Talking big (8)
18 Free from harm (4)
20 Perpendicular (5)
22 Laments (6)
23 This place (4)
24 Readers' group (4,4)

DOWN

1 Film director's cry (6)
2 Harshly critical (8)
3 Geometric shape (6)
4 Delegate (a task) (6)
5 People in general (4)
6 Sea fish (6)
13 Available supply (8)
15 Hip-hop singer (6)
16 Absorb (6)
17 Bacon joint (6)
19 Disperse (3,3)
21 Puts to some purpose (4)

Puzzle 12

ACROSS

- **7** ___ out, left petulantly (8)
- **8** Small particle (4)
- **9** Bury completely (6)
- **10** Quite difficult (6)
- **11** Shore stones (7)
- **13** Dish of mixed leaves (5)
- **15** Category (5)
- **17** To the soul (7)
- **19** Be filled (with) (6)
- **21** Issue forth (6)
- **23** Rabbit's tail (4)
- **24** Begin a journey (5,3)

DOWN

- **1** Stratagem (4)
- **2** Copper (hair) (6)
- **3** Brawl (7)
- **4** Revise for the press (4)
- **5** Mouth secretion (6)
- **6** Waterfront area in a city (8)
- **12** Delay, hinder (4,4)
- **14** Patella (7)
- **16** Bawdy (6)
- **18** Spies (6)
- **20** Smidgen, tad (4)
- **22** Bequest (4)

Puzzle 13

ACROSS

- **6** Currently continuing (7)
- **7** Extra payment (5)
- **9** Exploited (4)
- **10** Strongly built (4,4)
- **11** Makes of product (6)
- **13** Ship floor (4)
- **15** Log material (4)
- **16** Diverging from a central hub (6)
- **18** Sudden rainstorm (8)
- **21** Common metal (4)
- **22** Dissertation (5)
- **23** Pealing (7)

DOWN

- **1** Grind your teeth together (5)
- **2** Ground to dust (8)
- **3** Winter weather (4)
- **4** Reverberate (4)
- **5** Dandelion and ___, fizzy drink (7)
- **8** Shut (6)
- **12** Small in width (6)
- **13** Business relations (8)
- **14** Lone musician (7)
- **17** Sixteen ounces (5)
- **19** Orderly (4)
- **20** Spoil (4)

Puzzle 14

ACROSS

1 Lifeblood (7)
5 Circuit breaker (4)
8 Boasts triumphantly (5)
9 Deputy (5-2)
11 Frolic boisterously (4)
12 Embroil (8)
15 Malicious (5)
16 Budge (5)
19 Acting well in public (8)
21 Fermentation (4)
23 Dire (7)
25 Beaten path or road (5)
26 Russian monarch (4)
27 Sitting on (a horse) (7)

DOWN

2 Military step (4,5)
3 Simple to do (4)
4 Protective covering (6)
5 Fish's steering limb (3)
6 Gyrate (5)
7 Frighten (5)
10 Torpor (6)
13 Advance (2,7)
14 Soft rich fabric (6)
17 Hits (6)
18 Vigilant (5)
20 British noblemen (5)
22 Begin to move (4)
24 Male honorific (3)

Puzzle 15

ACROSS

1 School subject (5)
4 Lightly bob up and down (6)
10 Haughty pride (9)
11 Capture (3)
12 Black and white animal (5)
13 Blood vessel (6)
14 Be streets ahead (11)
18 Light colour (6)
20 Musical about an orphan (5)
23 Solid fuel cooker (3)
24 Supervise (5,4)
25 Weedy, weak (6)
26 Unusually (5)

DOWN

2 Cook's pinny (5)
3 Hollow-eyed (7)
5 Incapable (5)
6 Having no trademark (7)
7 Partakes of food (4)
8 Joyous (5)
9 Describe succinctly (11)
15 Oblivious (7)
16 Disconcerted (7)
17 Tired, fatigued (5)
19 Bath sheet (5)
21 Fresh, original (5)
22 Young elephant (4)

Puzzle 16

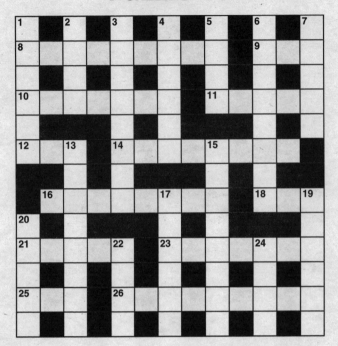

ACROSS

- **8** Compensate (9)
- **9** Visual organ (3)
- **10** Theory of the universe (3,4)
- **11** Stupid, daft (5)
- **12** Bark of a small dog (3)
- **14** Entire or whole (8)
- **16** Represent, symbolise (5,3)
- **18** Gullible person (3)
- **21** Very wavy (5)
- **23** Sound of a bird (7)
- **25** ___ de vie, brandy (3)
- **26** Topple (5,4)

DOWN

- **1** Filthy, soiled (6)
- **2** Utter musically (4)
- **3** Process of rubbing (8)
- **4** Bit of a scare (6)
- **5** Embryonic plant (4)
- **6** Maintain your cool! (4,4)
- **7** Blue-green gem (5)
- **13** Gradually diminish (5,3)
- **15** Pungent-tasting (8)
- **17** Element (6)
- **19** Cavernous, yawning (6)
- **20** Units of land (5)
- **22** Harness together (4)
- **24** Top of a car (4)

Puzzle 17

ACROSS

1 Scary (6)
4 Clamour (6)
9 More distinct (7)
10 Culpability (5)
11 Release your grip (3,2)
12 Arid (4,3)
13 Invited visitor (5)
15 Shovel (5)
20 Mistaken belief (7)
22 Spanish open square (5)
24 Arouse (5)
25 Simulate (7)
26 At all events (6)
27 Lay into (6)

DOWN

1 Laugh like a witch (6)
2 Apply (pressure) (5)
3 Religious ministers (7)
5 Of a city (5)
6 Plaited, intertwined (7)
7 Cheerio! (3-3)
8 Clan (5)
14 Ill-starred (7)
16 Sprinkles liberally (7)
17 Egypt's continent (6)
18 Woodland sprite (5)
19 Hooligan (6)
21 Largest artery (5)
23 Field of conflict (5)

Puzzle 18

ACROSS

1 Examine, research (5)
4 Remove hair (5)
10 Angels' instruments (5)
11 Soared up (7)
12 Stretch out on a bed (3,4)
13 Ice house (5)
14 Squeaky rodent (5)
16 Share the same view (5)
21 Brown uniform cloth (5)
23 Yet, but (7)
25 Guy-rope fastener (4,3)
26 Congregation (5)
27 Ooze (5)
28 Copper/zinc alloy (5)

DOWN

2 Submarine missile (7)
3 Dance party (5)
5 Roaring (7)
6 Caused by a bug (5)
7 Entirety (5)
8 Foul smell (5)
9 Supplemented item (3-2)
15 Dislocated (joint) (7)
17 Begrudging (7)
18 Move on ice (5)
19 Part of the leg (5)
20 Penniless (5)
22 Join, attach (5)
24 Crisp biscuit (5)

Puzzle 19

ACROSS

1 Chafing (7)
5 Discussion place (5)
8 Jottings (5)
9 Brighten (7)
10 Striking workers (7)
12 Shackles (5)
14 Awful experience (6)
16 Keyboard user (6)
18 Out of training (5)
19 Educated (7)
22 Animal raiser (7)
24 Army chaplain (5)
26 Dissuade, discourage (5)
27 Currency units (7)

DOWN

1 Accumulate (a debt) (3,2)
2 Small piece (3)
3 Emanate (5)
4 Lubrication (6)
5 Alter fraudulently (7)
6 Speed up (an engine) (3)
7 Attitude (7)
11 Husks of corn (5)
13 Pungent bulb (5)
14 Hitched (a lift) (7)
15 One who kills the bull (7)
17 Blazed up (6)
20 Fill with horror (5)
21 Wine residue (5)
23 Devour (3)
25 Gene code (inits) (3)

Puzzle 20

ACROSS

1 Injurious, harmful (6)
4 Rising (6)
8 'I' (3)
9 Fan (9)
11 Eagerness to possess (4)
12 Took off clothes (8)
15 Acknowledge a fault (9)
18 Domestic store (8)
19 Single-handed (4)
21 Concede, accept (9)
23 Beer barrel (3)
24 Concealing (6)
25 Melt down (fat) (6)

DOWN

1 Submissively (6)
2 Be quick (4,5)
3 Lacerate (4)
5 Forbid, veto (8)
6 Creativity (3)
7 Scorn (6)
10 Fragrant petals (3-6)
13 Heated in advance (3-6)
14 Slide on snow (8)
16 Char (6)
17 Lumberjack (6)
20 Pool, lake (4)
22 Chew the ___, ponder (3)

Puzzle 21

ACROSS

1 Trill (6)
4 Basic (diet) (6)
9 Meteorologist's device (4,5)
10 Rocky peak (3)
11 Sheltered area (3)
12 Recapture the past (5,4)
13 Steak (1-4)
15 Cut off (5)
20 Impression of a shoe (9)
22 Because of (3)
23 Terminate (3)
24 Sending up (6,3)
25 One's prime (6)
26 Filled with vapour (6)

DOWN

1 Distrustfully (6)
2 Elevate (5)
3 Make paler (7)
5 Pinch (5)
6 Affectionate moniker (3,4)
7 Archimedes' cry (6)
8 Hot but damp (5)
14 In a general sense (7)
16 Long died out (7)
17 Again (6)
18 Perilous (5)
19 Cunning (6)
21 Greek bread (5)
22 Region's plant life (5)

Puzzle 22

ACROSS

1 Prodigal, profligate (8)
6 Ribs or skulls, eg (5)
7 Blood-carrying tube (4)
8 Cable-free internet (2-2)
9 Alias (inits) (3)
10 Fired at (4)
11 Warmed and spiced (wine) (6)
13 Small domed spongy cake (6)
14 Not competent (6)
17 Jacuzzi (3,3)
18 Glance through (4)
20 Common drink (3)
21 Henpecks (4)
22 Shut noisily (4)
23 Affair (5)
24 Superseded (8)

DOWN

1 Female spouses (5)
2 By-product (4-3)
3 Unlike anything else (6)
4 Massage, squeeze (5)
5 (Look) with disdain (7)
6 Invoicing (7)
12 Passing through a riddle (7)
13 Subdue by penance (7)
15 Fastened with a clasp (7)
16 Martial art (4,2)
17 Nun's garment (5)
19 Wanderer (5)

Puzzle 23

ACROSS

1 Sad (8)
5 Masticate (4)
9 Data entry (5)
10 Aquatic competitor (7)
11 Terrible fate (4)
12 Be towed by a speedboat (5-3)
14 Thread (6)
15 Air travellers' ailment (3,3)
18 Film setting (8)
20 Unguent (4)
22 Stimulating (7)
23 Unblocked (5)
24 Aristocratic title (4)
25 Strict political thinking (8)

DOWN

1 Desiccated (5)
2 Annihilate (4,3)
3 Pare down (3)
4 Swagger (6)
6 Family houses (5)
7 Cautionary (7)
8 Gnarled (7)
13 Facial air hole (7)
14 Degree of excellence (7)
16 Release your grip (5,2)
17 Made at a smithy (6)
19 Single seat (5)
21 Clemency (5)
23 Pigeon's call (3)

Puzzle 24

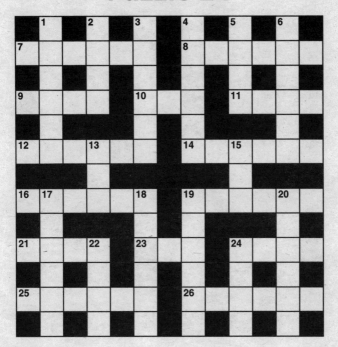

ACROSS

7 Find, unearth (4,2)
8 Temptresses (6)
9 Casserole (4)
10 Ceremonial sphere (3)
11 52 weeks (4)
12 Baby swan (6)
14 Beginning of a baby (6)
16 Turn pale (6)
19 Ill-fated (6)
21 Stopper for a bath (4)
23 Silent, tight-lipped (3)
24 Shall we? (4)
25 Pertaining to mail (6)
26 Spheres of action (6)

DOWN

1 Rightly (6)
2 Recognised (4)
3 Decline to participate (3,3)
4 Of service (6)
5 Medical photo (1-3)
6 Devious (6)
13 Fool (3)
15 Currant cake (3)
17 Cling (4,2)
18 Specifically (6)
19 Glass kitchen container (3-3)
20 Bit-part actors (6)
22 Pluck, bottle (4)
24 Tells fibs (4)

Puzzle 25

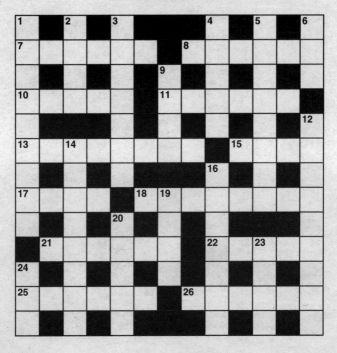

ACROSS

7 Admit to a post (6)
8 Extinguished (a fire) (3,3)
10 Enter data (3,2)
11 Separate (6)
13 Countermand (8)
15 Domain, sector (4)
17 On any occasion (4)
18 Horticulturist (8)
21 Passionless (6)
22 Bulbous root (5)
25 Very hot (6)
26 Lookalike (6)

DOWN

1 Foot fighter! (4-5)
2 Tense (4)
3 View, vista (7)
4 Voluptuous (5)
5 Come close to (6,2)
6 Money dispenser (inits) (3)
9 Worshipped film star (4)
12 Salon appliance (9)
14 Optical solution (3-5)
16 Published issue (7)
19 Political adviser (4)
20 Extreme pain (5)
23 Babies' aprons (4)
24 iPhone facility (abbrev.)(3)

Puzzle 26

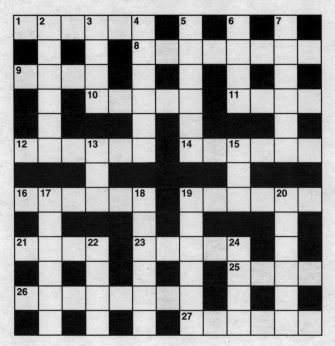

ACROSS

1 Moonlight ___, piano piece (6)
8 Turning into (8)
9 Average (2-2)
10 Shine faintly (5)
11 Pastime (4)
12 Narrow sea channel (6)
14 Agreeably (6)
16 Entirely, totally (6)
19 Excluded (6)
21 Overlook (4)
23 Seeing that (5)
25 Swelling (4)
26 Co-operate (4,4)
27 Simply (6)

DOWN

2 Woodwind player (6)
3 Eager, expectant (4)
4 Miserable, woeful (6)
5 Business ability (6)
6 Polluted air (4)
7 Beast (6)
13 Every one of (3)
15 Any ill-bred dog (3)
17 Familiar, domestic (6)
18 Bootlicker (3-3)
19 Make a mistake (6)
20 Tooth coating (6)
22 Children's playthings (4)
24 'Dutch disease' trees (4)

Puzzle 27

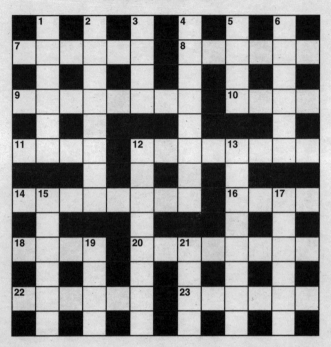

ACROSS

7 Fiddle (6)
8 Time-telling word (6)
9 Demolishing (8)
10 Hoodlum (4)
11 Minicab (4)
12 Opinions (8)
14 Be reluctant to act (4,4)
16 Red jewel (4)
18 Electric cable (4)
20 Wash off soap from (5,3)
22 1588 Spanish fleet (6)
23 Landowner, historically (6)

DOWN

1 Mountain range (6)
2 Showing a sudden light (8)
3 Against (4)
4 Album of ditties (8)
5 Piece of ground (4)
6 Clear (of charges) (6)
12 Rest period at work (3,5)
13 Very lovely (8)
15 Large bird enclosure (6)
17 Ill-defined (6)
19 Academic test (4)
21 Deep Scottish loch (4)

Puzzle 28

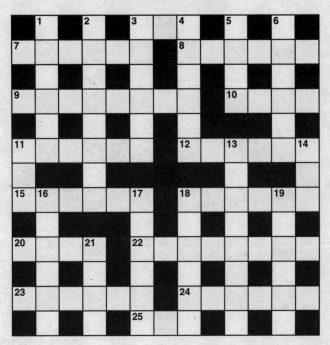

ACROSS

3 Infant's chin-cloth (3)
7 Purpose (6)
8 Strike, collide (6)
9 Gradually cease (5,3)
10 Hammer, eg (4)
11 Having an argument (6)
12 Conditional release (6)
15 Type of lightning (6)
18 Broadcast (6)
20 Betting chances (4)
22 Purpose, use (8)
23 Firearm (6)
24 Naval flag (6)
25 However (3)

DOWN

1 Sound of sobbing (6)
2 Black spill in the sea (3,5)
3 Fit in (6)
4 Circus tent (3,3)
5 Petty quarrel, tiff (4)
6 Place to learn (6)
11 Flying armed service (inits) (3)
13 Car try-out (4,4)
14 Conclusion (3)
16 Appoint as a minister (6)
17 Expertly, skilfully (6)
18 Lady's hat tied with ribbons (6)
19 Sufficient, plenty (6)
21 Position for a building (4)

Puzzle 29

ACROSS

1 Awkward, ungainly (6)
4 Wallet for papers (6)
9 Puts into words (9)
10 Salty oriental sauce (3)
11 Make mistakes (3)
12 Tool with a flame (9)
13 Dentures (5)
15 Break into pieces (5)
20 Conceited, arrogant (3-6)
22 Automobile (3)
23 Iowa's country (inits) (3)
24 Footwear fasteners (9)
25 Slightly intoxicated (6)
26 Igloo dweller (6)

DOWN

1 Smart, brainy (6)
2 Opposite of 'lower' (5)
3 Fizzy sweet powder (7)
5 Start, beginning (5)
6 Wants, wishes for (7)
7 Musical beat (6)
8 ___ Villa, football club (5)
14 London's country (7)
16 Mixes up (7)
17 Kidnap (6)
18 IT storage device (1,1-3)
19 Renaissance mural (6)
21 Artist's stand (5)
22 Prickly desert plants (5)

Puzzle 30

ACROSS

1 Split-lens spectacles (8)
6 Was concerned (5)
7 Ship ___, pirates' cry (4)
8 Disentangle (4)
9 Alien spacecraft (inits) (3)
10 Sea movement (4)
11 Of light, lowered (6)
13 Present-day (6)
14 ___ bomb, nuclear explosive (6)
17 Coached, tutored (6)
18 Unit of speed at sea (4)
20 Lavatory (3)
21 Corner, narrow recess (4)
22 Stare lustfully (4)
23 Sway back and forth (5)
24 Issued (a CD) (8)

DOWN

1 Brag (5)
2 Inundated with water (7)
3 Green, yellow or red pulse (6)
4 Pleased with yourself (5)
5 Really stupid (7)
6 Perpetrates (a crime) (7)
12 Quarrelling (7)
13 Snail or slug, eg (7)
15 Runs, supervises (7)
16 Type of metal plating (6)
17 Poisonous (5)
19 Walk (on) (5)

Puzzle 31

ACROSS

1 Drinks cooler (3,4)
5 In foliage (5)
9 Rural relative? (7,6)
10 Run across (4,4)
11 Exude (4)
12 Hiatus (9)
16 Old wound mark (4)
17 Be cautious (4,4)
19 Male head of a home (3,2,3,5)
21 Resource (5)
22 To no purpose (7)

DOWN

2 Group of voices (6)
3 Kitchen utensil (3-6)
4 British nobleman (5)
6 French for 'water' (3)
7 With tight curls (6)
8 Cylinder of paper (6)
11 Outmoded (3-6)
13 Being (6)
14 Vast seas (6)
15 Crucial time (6)
18 Human leg joints (5)
20 Low number (3)

Puzzle 32

ACROSS

7 Hotel chain (6)
8 Stuck-up, conceited (6)
10 Adult females (5)
11 Floppy, limp (6)
13 Proofs of payment (8)
15 Hold firmly (4)
17 Number of a cat's lives (4)
18 Shenanigans (6-2)
21 Force, browbeat (6)
22 Divided (5)
25 Sharp and cold (of wind) (6)
26 Be indecisive (6)

DOWN

1 Washing in a cubicle (9)
2 Fairly thin (4)
3 Canadian policeman (7)
4 ___ Jack, flag (5)
5 Variety-show hosts (8)
6 Cheerio (3)
9 Revise text (4)
12 Bachelor girls? (9)
14 Makes by mixing (8)
16 Ill person (7)
19 Slippery with grease (4)
20 Passed (time) (5)
23 Prolonged dull pain (4)
24 UK TV company (inits) (3)

Puzzle 33

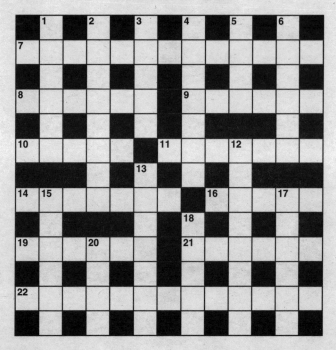

ACROSS

7 Self-centred conduct (13)
8 Organ close to the stomach (6)
9 Attractively (6)
10 Electricity tower (5)
11 Inspire fervour (7)
14 Book covering (7)
16 Increased quantity (5)
19 Part of a jacket (6)
21 Obtrude (4,2)
22 Unauthorised walk-out (7,6)

DOWN

1 Irascible (6)
2 Back way (4,4)
3 Large African cats (5)
4 Swelling (up) (7)
5 Quiche (4)
6 OT hymns (6)
12 Low-waisted trousers (8)
13 Protection for the patella (4-3)
15 Embedded (6)
17 Swindles (6)
18 Bottomless gulf (5)
20 Gentle whirlpool (4)

Puzzle 34

ACROSS

1 Grade of colour (5)
4 Be successful (2,3)
10 Fold-up mattress (4-3)
11 Bejewelled headband (5)
12 Hard fruit kernels (4)
13 Contemptuous (8)
16 Token, ticket (6)
17 Preserved in tins (6)
20 Logical (8)
21 Wheel covering (4)
23 Bay of Naples isle (5)
25 Weeping trees (7)
26 Theatre platform (5)
27 Cheerful, jaunty (5)

DOWN

2 Unpleasant fact (4,5)
3 Amount due (4)
5 Eruption (of disease) (8)
6 Alias (inits) (3)
7 Picturesque (6)
8 Decree, order (5)
9 Partition (4)
14 Decorative stitching (9)
15 Embarking (8)
18 Smart, stylish (6)
19 Tintin's faithful dog (5)
20 Male chicken (4)
22 Layer of drifting ice (4)
24 Earthenware vessel (3)

Puzzle 35

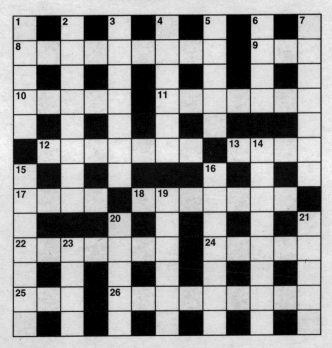

ACROSS

8 Affectionate couple (9)
9 Go (for) (3)
10 Cup ___, deciding match (5)
11 ___ mantis, insect (7)
12 Edible molluscs (7)
13 Biblical paradise (4)
17 Move on wheels (4)
18 Entrails (7)
22 Winter sports event (3,4)
24 Lukewarm (5)
25 Large vase (3)
26 Pummelling (9)

DOWN

1 Gap or opening (5)
2 Ultimate (8)
3 Annul (7)
4 Drive forward (6)
5 Commonly experienced (5)
6 Hindu mystic (4)
7 Scaffold (in a theatre) (7)
14 With excise charged (4-4)
15 Go over, revise (5,2)
16 Drifting debris (7)
19 Encroach, force upon (6)
20 Child's word for 'stomach' (5)
21 Saw, maxim (5)
23 Pubs (4)

Puzzle 36

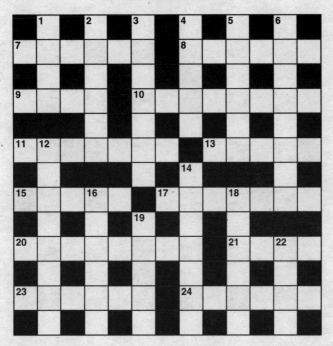

ACROSS

7 Quietened (6)
8 Cause, motive (6)
9 Range of saxophone (4)
10 Occupying forces (8)
11 Concise and witty saying (7)
13 Serious, solemn (5)
15 Anti-wrinkle drug (5)
17 Squats (down) (7)
20 Send to ___, ostracise (8)
21 Police officers (4)
23 Rickety, dangerous (6)
24 Spay, castrate (6)

DOWN

1 Toss (4)
2 Gather in numbers (6)
3 Red ___, butterfly (7)
4 Show to be true (5)
5 ___ to, indulge (6)
6 Motorist's partner (2-6)
12 Deep, intense (8)
14 Easily floating (7)
16 Single (ticket) (3-3)
18 Create (a fuss) (4,2)
19 Tough metal (5)
22 Pastry dishes (4)

Puzzle 37

ACROSS

1 Sympathetic (4,8)
9 Officer in training (5)
10 Finger idly (7)
11 Transcendental (8)
12 Hard of hearing (4)
14 Luggage handler (6)
15 Featherbrained (6)
18 Furthermore (4)
20 Facial bruise (5,3)
23 Offer too much for (7)
24 Come after (5)
25 Decide in advance (12)

DOWN

2 Ultimate consumer (3-4)
3 Criss-crossed with bars (8)
4 Desk accessory (2-4)
5 Soreness (4)
6 Edge slowly (5)
7 Cook in boiling oil (4-3)
8 Floating waste (4)
13 Frozen confection (3,5)
14 Thick green or yellow broth (3,4)
16 Disloyalty (7)
17 Pawn (6)
19 Beleaguering of a town (5)
21 Always (4)
22 Skilled (4)

Puzzle 38

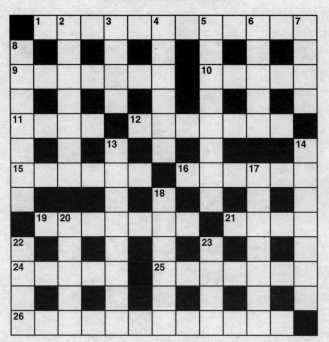

ACROSS

1 Moving-in party (5-7)
9 Isolated, excluded (4,3)
10 Warning sound (5)
11 Smell strongly (4)
12 Cut with shears (7)
15 Intact (6)
16 Spanish rice dish (6)
19 Cheap purchase (7)
21 Thrust with a knife (4)
24 Throw out (5)
25 Subcontract (4,3)
26 Intricate affair (12)

DOWN

2 Rich (7)
3 Chimney deposit (4)
4 Burble (6)
5 Come again (8)
6 Mindless (5)
7 Willing, plucky (4)
8 Unlawful dictator (7)
13 Intimidate (8)
14 Holy day (7)
17 Disappoint (3,4)
18 Irregular (6)
20 Accomplished (5)
22 In this place (4)
23 Pare (4)

Puzzle 39

ACROSS

1 Application (5)
4 Fit (7)
9 Place in a cot (3,2,3)
10 Middle of a church (4)
11 Exit door (3,3)
12 Unable to live for ever (6)
13 Excuse (13)
17 Birthday-cake light (6)
19 Harsh, rough (6)
21 Forewarning (4)
22 Crapulous (4-4)
23 Fabric offcut (7)
24 Go by bike (5)

DOWN

2 Finnish steam bath (5)
3 Dismissive remark (3,4)
5 Prevalent locally (7)
6 Solitary person (5)
7 Make an attempt (4,1,2)
8 Be next to (4)
14 Carrying no weapons (7)
15 Renew (7)
16 Brewing-vessel cover (3,4)
18 Durable twilled cloth (5)
19 Cheats, diddles (4)
20 Incantation (5)

Puzzle 40

ACROSS

1 Personification (7)
4 Rotisserie (4)
9 Gossip (7)
11 In the middle of (5)
12 Run off to wed (5)
13 Hard bath sponge (6)
15 Absolved (6)
17 Get (6)
19 Nautical craft (6)
20 Terrible, dreadful (5)
23 Protector (5)
24 Swimming-pool section (4,3)
25 Portal (4)
26 Treason (7)

DOWN

2 Keyboard instrument (5)
3 Short-lived insect (6)
5 Commensurate (3,4)
6 Roman item of attire (4)
7 Steals (7)
8 Shaving requisite (5,5)
10 Push out of the way (5,5)
14 Subsume (7)
16 Stylish (7)
18 Mud (6)
21 Devil (5)
22 Very eager (4)

Puzzle 41

ACROSS

1 Line of colour (6)
4 Group of flats (5)
8 Unexpected benefit (5)
9 Enlighten (7)
10 Lee (7)
11 Of the mouth (4)
12 Churchyard tree (3)
14 Russian ruler (4)
15 All singularly (4)
18 Mass of water (3)
21 Pay attention to (4)
23 Manual air pump (7)
25 Sweepstakes (7)
26 Cunningly escape from (5)
27 Bowed, bent (5)
28 Declares (6)

DOWN

1 Indian spiced pastry (6)
2 Senior Girl Guides (7)
3 Trays (8)
4 Azure (4)
5 Broadcasting live (2,3)
6 Ardently (6)
7 Passenger boat (5)
13 In good order (4-4)
16 Hoop and mallet game (7)
17 Angelic child (6)
19 Maltreatment (5)
20 Estimate (6)
22 Gamine (5)
24 Whip (4)

Puzzle 42

ACROSS

7 Longing for (8)
8 Cheerless, severe (4)
10 Lie partly upon (7)
11 Yell, roar (5)
12 Shortly (4)
13 Extreme unkindness (7)
16 Rural and unspoilt (7)
18 Between (4)
22 Pertaining to a town (5)
24 Harmonious (7)
25 Metal spike (4)
26 Not fastened (door) (8)

DOWN

1 Hateful, repulsive (6)
2 Small planet (8)
3 Cook by radiant heat (5)
4 Hidden rifleman (6)
5 Three performers (4)
6 Metal worker (5)
9 Crooked (5)
14 Meekness (8)
15 Propel with one finger (5)
17 Resistant (to disease) (6)
19 Ten-year period (6)
20 Subdivision of a play (5)
21 Liquid in veins (5)
23 Bride's face cover (4)

Puzzle 43

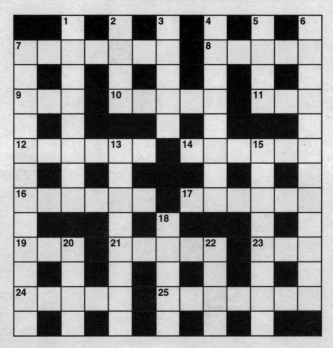

ACROSS

7 In the fresh air (7)
8 Objet d'art (5)
9 Sensory organ (3)
10 Queen's favourite dog (5)
11 Gullible person (3)
12 Close, airless (6)
14 On a ship (6)
16 Lose (6)
17 Japanese hostess (6)
19 Hit (a ball) (3)
21 From now (5)
23 Lowing sound (3)
24 Reception area (5)
25 Educated (7)

DOWN

1 Rider's footrests (8)
2 Flat token (4)
3 Orchard fruits (5)
4 Write quickly (8)
5 Metric unit of weight (4)
6 Uncut gem (5,7)
7 Make too easy (12)
13 Plumage (8)
15 Feigning (8)
18 State of being one (5)
20 Young men (4)
22 Important test (4)

Puzzle 44

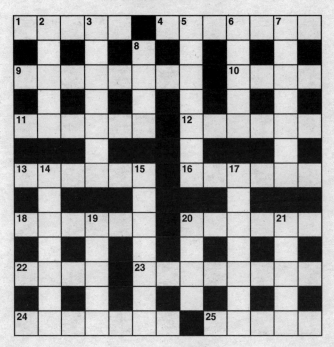

ACROSS

1 Non-verse writing (5)
4 Near view (5-2)
9 Hotel grade (4-4)
10 All square (4)
11 Shortened (6)
12 Mass entry (6)
13 Rudimentary calculator (6)
16 Freely (6)
18 Of the universe (6)
20 Royal title (6)
22 Scottish tribe (4)
23 Sit on (eggs) (8)
24 Intransigent (7)
25 Welsh name for Wales (5)

DOWN

2 Large African animal (5)
3 Doubting person (7)
5 Lying in wait (7)
6 Ledge (5)
7 Ill-balanced (7)
8 Version of poker (4)
14 Cooked on a grill (7)
15 Pulling-in power (7)
17 Jovially (7)
19 Note in music (5)
20 Choose (4)
21 Purvey food (5)

Puzzle 45

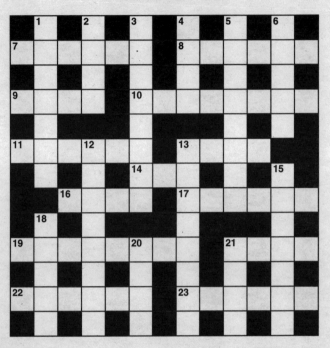

ACROSS

7 Chief male servant (6)
8 Portugal's continent (6)
9 Area of land in water (4)
10 Fusspot (8)
11 Spiced sausage (6)
13 Supermarket (4)
14 Convent sister (3)
16 Wooden shoe (4)
17 Go to a restaurant (3,3)
19 On any occasion (8)
21 Plum ___, dessert (4)
22 Cattle feed (6)
23 Animal and plant life, eg (6)

DOWN

1 ___ roulette, deadly game (7)
2 Joy, delight (4)
3 Tying up before cooking (8)
4 Speciality food store (4)
5 Escaped from jail (5,3)
6 Drive too fast (5)
12 Provided that (2,4,2)
13 Scornful (8)
15 Experiences troubles (7)
18 Beat strongly (5)
20 Turn sharply (4)
21 Romantic meeting (4)

Puzzle 46

ACROSS

6 Making cold (8)
8 Chinese boat (4)
10 Without lighting (5)
11 In great quantity (6)
13 Upper House peer (4)
14 Transfer (4,4)
16 Recent resident (8)
19 Birds of the night (4)
22 Quarter of a whole (6)
23 Nurse or guardian (5)
25 Cambridgeshire marshes (4)
26 Put in jail, detain (8)

DOWN

1 Expanse of brushwood (9)
2 Fabric (5)
3 Puzzle, mystery (6)
4 Paper size (6)
5 The heavens (3)
7 Lazy person (5)
9 Single leaf of grass (5)
12 Under tight control (2,1,6)
15 Sixty-minute periods (5)
17 Attempting to win over (6)
18 Disinter, unearth (6)
20 Parts of a sentence (5)
21 Mark, scratch (5)
24 Below par (3)

Puzzle 47

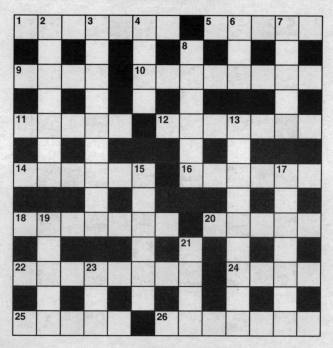

ACROSS

1 Sewing aid (7)
5 Marshy region (5)
9 Broad smile (4)
10 Interest charge (4,4)
11 Gambling game (5)
12 Robin Hood's weapon (7)
14 Last (6)
16 Cold-shoulder (6)
18 Socialises (with) (7)
20 Sales rep (5)
22 Ready (for) (6,2)
24 Part of the eye (4)
25 Garden dwarf? (5)
26 Large military unit (7)

DOWN

2 Fishing spear (7)
3 Shop-window dummy (9)
4 Part of the ear (4)
6 Armed conflict (3)
7 Saying, adage (5)
8 Within a building (6)
13 Be unneeded (2,7)
15 Typify (6)
17 Favoured (7)
19 Atlantic, say (5)
21 Goad into action (4)
23 Dash into violently (3)

Puzzle 48

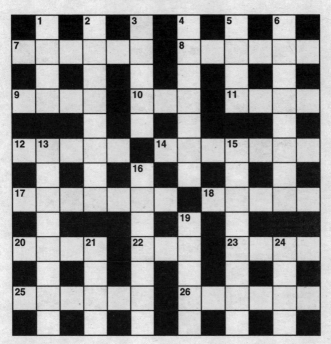

ACROSS

7 Bends forward and down (6)
8 Draw up at the roadside (4,2)
9 Nautical beam (4)
10 Blunder (3)
11 Leaves (4)
12 Puff of smell (5)
14 Vehicle record (7)
17 Accumulate (5,2)
18 Tighten by turning (5)
20 Produced young (4)
22 Triumph (3)
23 Aromatic herb (4)
25 Spread out (a carpet) (6)
26 Open level lands (6)

DOWN

1 Place your foot (4)
2 Dreadful, ghastly (8)
3 Michaelmas daisy (5)
4 Garden bird (7)
5 Strike (4)
6 Wearing, tedious (8)
13 Tea or toddy, eg (3,5)
15 Position in the rear (4,4)
16 Go out of control (3,4)
19 Shoot from cover (5)
21 Portal (4)
24 Work crew (4)

Puzzle 49

ACROSS

1 Thick alcoholic drink (3-3)
5 Shakes (a tail) (4)
8 Following as a consequence (9)
9 Part of a circle (3)
11 Knitting material (4)
12 In a state of disorder (8)
14 Gently amuse (6)
16 Hunting bird (6)
18 World Wide Web (8)
19 Skin blemish (4)
22 Idol, deity (3)
23 Deliver a baby (4,5)
24 Wooden strip (4)
25 To some degree (6)

DOWN

2 Relish (5)
3 Void, invalid (4)
4 Poor-quality (photo) (6)
5 Canal (8)
6 Diagram (7)
7 Waistband pull-cord (10)
10 Fairground stall (7,3)
13 Acceptable (3,5)
15 Fortress, castle (7)
17 Dam-building rodent (6)
20 Woman's wallet (5)
21 Aid illegally (4)

Puzzle 50

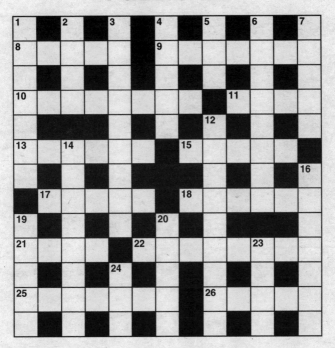

ACROSS

8 Party dance (5)
9 Confer (7)
10 Foppish triviality (8)
11 Tie (4)
13 Fish-eating bird (6)
15 Belonging to those people (5)
17 Horse noise (5)
18 Blot (6)
21 Showily creative (4)
22 Apartment sharer (8)
25 Accumulated (5,2)
26 Elbow prod (5)

DOWN

1 Drifting frozen mass (3,4)
2 Firmly against (4)
3 Small red soft fruit (9)
4 Love deeply (5)
5 Burnt residue (3)
6 Cleansed (8)
7 Stage whisper (5)
12 TV show's title music (5,4)
14 Style for long hair (8)
16 Disconnected (7)
19 Roadside parking area (3-2)
20 Gradient, incline (5)
23 Political assistant (4)
24 And the rest (abbrev.) (3)

Puzzle 51

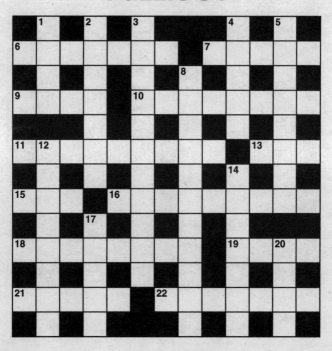

ACROSS

6 How come? (4,3)
7 Forest path (5)
9 Move in water (4)
10 Pity (8)
11 Sleep outdoors (4,5)
13 Be too curious (3)
15 Had some food (3)
16 Household goods (9)
18 Eruption, explosion (8)
19 Insipid, dull (4)
21 Weighty (5)
22 Rapaciousness (7)

DOWN

1 Defrost (4)
2 Dammed (7)
3 First course (4,7)
4 Short holiday (5)
5 Undecided person (8)
8 Using clever ideas (11)
12 Trespasser (8)
14 Natural height (7)
17 At a higher point (5)
20 Medieval knight's club (4)

Puzzle 52

ACROSS

1 Picked, chose (8)
5 Gambling counter (4)
8 Sharpshooter (8)
9 Dumbfound (4)
11 Indian robe (4)
12 Popeye's vegetable (7)
14 Hate, detest (6)
16 Short necklace (6)
18 Dish holder (7)
19 Elliptic (4)
22 Coaching houses (4)
23 Boarding-house (8)
24 Takes food (4)
25 Surprised (8)

DOWN

1 Not all (4)
2 Maggot, eg (5)
3 Liquid funds (4,2,4)
4 Of time, pass (6)
6 Give like for like (3,4)
7 Large black cats (8)
10 Seafood retailer (10)
13 Package-holiday variety (3-5)
15 Not in favour of (7)
17 Test (3,3)
20 Rescind (5)
21 Pre-owned (4)

Puzzle 53

ACROSS

1 Top floor (5,6)
8 Use a vacuum cleaner (6)
9 Favourite drink (6)
10 Cock a snook at (4)
11 French red wine (8)
13 Small bits of land (5)
15 Manage, cope (3,2)
18 Glue (8)
19 Session (4)
20 Communicate, relate (6)
21 Envelop (6)
22 Be traded (6,5)

DOWN

2 Declared publicly (9)
3 Diplomat (5)
4 Vigorously cleans (6)
5 Loud protest (6)
6 Embrace as a cause (7)
7 Alluring (4)
12 Dissolute (9)
14 Ocular hair (7)
16 Young feline (6)
17 Renter, tenant (6)
18 Centre of rotation (4)
19 Costa ___, holiday area (5)

Puzzle 54

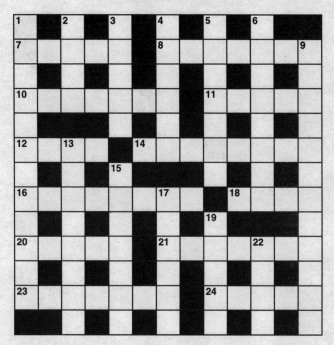

ACROSS

7 Hard to chew (5)
8 Nightclub doorman (7)
10 Come across (3,4)
11 Toy people to dress (5)
12 Lazily (4)
14 Caution, warn (8)
16 Fuel-processing plant (8)
18 Advanced in years (4)
20 Item's worth (5)
21 Numerical (display) (7)
23 Work out (7)
24 Allow to enter (3,2)

DOWN

1 Beginning again (8,4)
2 Swivel (4)
3 Switch tracks (train) (5)
4 Out of the country (6)
5 Open-air (7)
6 Burning with water (8)
9 Deferring to a later date (12)
13 Lethargic (8)
15 Restrainedly (7)
17 Variety of bean (6)
19 Flexible (5)
22 Large bag (4)

Puzzle 55

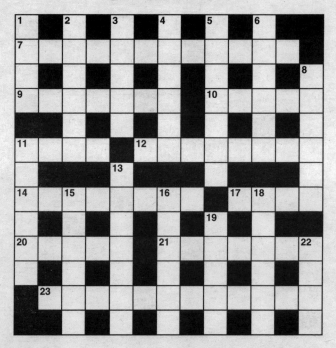

ACROSS

7 Not sorry (12)
9 Proper behaviour (7)
10 Proof of whereabouts (5)
11 Drop (4)
12 Hired murderer (8)
14 Cloth for drying (3,5)
17 Before long (4)
20 Urge (3,2)
21 Defensive wall (7)
23 Incontrovertibly (12)

DOWN

1 Kitty (4)
2 Lovable rogue (6)
3 Poisonous snake (5)
4 Space, universe (6)
5 Prison escape (7)
6 Large towns (6)
8 Register on arrival (4,2)
11 Feed up for slaughter (6)
13 Receptacle for money (4,3)
15 Fisherman (6)
16 Make a raised design (6)
18 In the vicinity (6)
19 Pomp, splendour (5)
22 Piano levers (4)

Puzzle 56

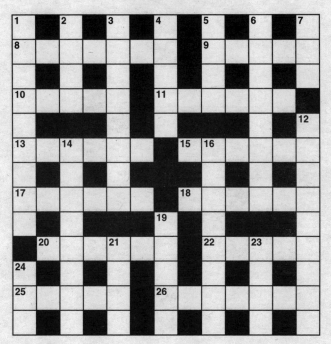

ACROSS

8 Rooked (7)
9 Spouse's relative (2-3)
10 Variety of bingo (5)
11 Ravenous insect (6)
13 Particular point in time (6)
15 Get rid of (6)
17 One who counts votes (6)
18 Betting term (4-2)
20 Fools about (6)
22 Reviving medicine (5)
25 Colour of jet (5)
26 Improvement (7)

DOWN

1 Prohibited (area) (3-6)
2 Corrupt or curved (4)
3 Obtain by cadging (8)
4 Fully grown (5)
5 Metal in brass (4)
6 Greek and Latin studies (8)
7 Wonderment (3)
12 Communication method (5,4)
14 Dense fruity bread (4,4)
16 E-number (8)
19 Wrest power from (5)
21 Ship's stern trail (4)
23 Maritime force (4)
24 Decline (3)

Puzzle 57

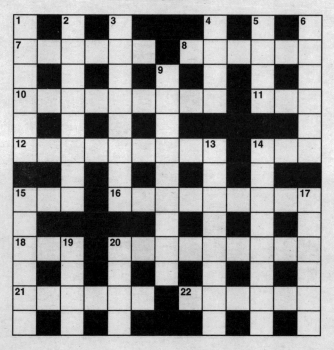

ACROSS

- **7** Frightened or sorry (6)
- **8** Unhurriedly (6)
- **10** Cut up methodically (9)
- **11** Disorderly crowd (3)
- **12** Frothy dairy drink (4-5)
- **14** Contend (3)
- **15** Saucepan cover (3)
- **16** Involved in conflict (9)
- **18** Craving (3)
- **20** Principal plumbing pipe (5,4)
- **21** Mending (6)
- **22** Batch (3,3)

DOWN

- **1** Unsystematic (6)
- **2** Grappled, struggled (8)
- **3** Publican (8)
- **4** Piece of turf (4)
- **5** Move in the water (4)
- **6** Cheerio! (3-3)
- **9** Health-spa treatment (5,4)
- **13** Outside (8)
- **14** Worth money (8)
- **15** Make redundant (3,3)
- **17** Indicate (6)
- **19** Immediately after (4)
- **20** Close one eye briefly (4)

Puzzle 58

ACROSS

1 Round wooden pin (5)
4 Say nothing! (4,3)
8 Found, initiate (5,2)
9 Young fowl (5)
10 Exclude (4)
11 Spun trap (3)
12 Prohibit (4)
15 Energy, force (6)
16 Authority on a subject (6)
19 Frolic (4)
21 Incise (3)
22 Keen, eager (4)
26 Arctic dwelling (5)
27 Metal in its raw form (4,3)
28 Pitching (7)
29 Coalesced (5)

DOWN

1 Dance party (5)
2 Zigzagging (7)
3 Behind time (4)
4 Breakfast fish (6)
5 Apiece (4)
6 Corn crop (5)
7 Pretend, falsely claim (4,3)
13 Milk container (3)
14 Watering hole (3)
15 Wood lacquer (7)
17 Shifty (7)
18 Official decision (6)
20 Human tooth (5)
23 Lingering fear (5)
24 Hindu teacher (4)
25 Top (of the mouth) (4)

Puzzle 59

ACROSS

1 Pied ___, rat exterminator (5)
4 Nonsense (7)
8 Invention (7)
9 Deface (5)
10 Fifty-two weeks (4)
11 Hop-rich beer (3)
12 Indian garment (4)
15 Weak (6)
16 Emitting smoke (6)
19 Small nail (4)
21 Gremlin, glitch (3)
22 Exploits (4)
26 Fake (5)
27 From dawn till dusk (3-4)
28 Showing the way (7)
29 Harpoon (5)

DOWN

1 Bloated (5)
2 Carton (7)
3 Heavy drizzle (4)
4 Carrying-strap (6)
5 General sense (4)
6 Fragrance (5)
7 Abetting (7)
13 Strand of wool (3)
14 Put your arms around (3)
15 Decisive (7)
17 On a shop's shelves (2-5)
18 Small canine breed (3,3)
20 Shanghai's country (5)
23 Sweetening agent (5)
24 Firmly against (4)
25 Views (4)

Puzzle 60

ACROSS

1 Attempt to anticipate (6-5)
9 Aces or jacks, eg (5)
10 Suppliers of flour (7)
11 Popular shrub (7)
12 Abide (5)
13 Employ once more (5)
15 Familiar, recognised (5)
20 Long firearm (5)
22 Mental pictures (7)
24 Twisted (7)
25 Grant admission to (3,2)
26 Salon worker (11)

DOWN

2 Aural pain (7)
3 Fashion chain store (5)
4 Abase (6)
5 Empty of cargo (7)
6 Undressed kidskin (5)
7 Mock, ridicule (5)
8 OT song (5)
14 Person talking (7)
16 Twist together (7)
17 Gap, chink (5)
18 Delay, obstruct (6)
19 Being untruthful (5)
21 Plant life (5)
23 Book of maps (5)

Puzzle 61

ACROSS

1 Bewildered (7)
5 Old Russian ruler (4)
10 Feathers on a bird (7)
11 Stupid fellow (5)
12 Arrest (5)
13 Cows' milk organs (6)
15 Given a new life (6)
17 Fabric merchant (6)
19 Rotten, decomposed (6)
20 Big ___, New York (5)
23 Jewish leader (5)
24 Cameo appearance (3,4)
25 Tiresome nuisance (4)
26 Tendency (7)

DOWN

2 Mature person (5)
3 Airhead (12)
4 Prolong (3,3)
6 Rider's footrest (7)
7 Wheel marks (4)
8 Apparition (7)
9 Playschool (12)
14 Inhuman treatment (7)
16 Cry noisily (7)
18 Fit to consume (6)
21 Clearly evident (5)
22 Coastal crustacean (4)

Puzzle 62

ACROSS

1 Money back (6)
4 Builds, fashions (6)
9 Chilly, cold (7)
10 Former (5)
11 Escape (4)
12 Second admission (2-5)
14 Fervid (6)
16 Japanese hostess (6)
19 Nightclub doorman (7)
21 Trailing plant (4)
23 Provoke (5)
24 Larva of a frog (7)
25 Sign up (6)
26 Brainy scientist (6)

DOWN

1 Shade of pink (4)
2 Edged with cloth (7)
3 Female relation (5)
5 Sated, full (7)
6 Dally teasingly (5)
7 Instant bronzer (5,3)
8 Gift of the Magi (5)
13 Scout gathering (8)
15 Central part of a cell (7)
17 Farewell party (4-3)
18 'Head' on beer (5)
20 Commonplace (5)
21 Cassette film (5)
22 Child, in Scotland (4)

Puzzle 63

ACROSS

1 Sculpted figure (6)
5 In a remote place (3-3)
8 Drug (8)
9 Tired-looking (4)
10 Hackney carriage (4)
11 Midway break (8)
12 Saying nothing (5-6)
15 Stick-thin (4,4)
18 Slothful (4)
20 Rouse (4)
21 Puncture (4,4)
22 Betting term (4-2)
23 Inspire affection (6)

DOWN

2 Coronet (5)
3 Gathering (7)
4 Be humiliated (3,4)
5 Aspect, view (5)
6 One who uses oars (5)
7 Ahead (7)
12 Wrenched (7)
13 Place apart (7)
14 Issued (7)
16 British noblemen (5)
17 Fairy-like (5)
19 Newly hatched insect (5)

Puzzle 64

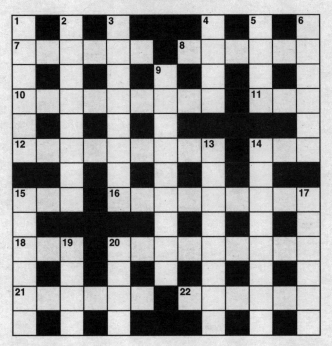

ACROSS

7 Takings or wages (6)
8 Predatory fishes (6)
10 Very finely sliced (5-4)
11 Fairy-like being (3)
12 Put back in office (9)
14 Friend (3)
15 Gearwheel (3)
16 Excessively (2,7)
18 Point, gist (3)
20 Belittle (9)
21 Put in a box (6)
22 Kick of a gun (6)

DOWN

1 Inspector, observer (6)
2 Expressing contempt (8)
3 Food of the gods (8)
4 Steer clear of (4)
5 Oak, ash, for example (4)
6 Of service (6)
9 Low price (9)
13 Having been taught (8)
14 Revealing (garment) (8)
15 Horse's gait (6)
17 Self-effacingly (6)
19 Male rabbit (4)
20 Shallow vessel (4)

Puzzle 65

ACROSS

1 Engagement calendars (7)
5 Talk (with a friend) (4)
10 Bring (pressure) to bear (5)
11 Give up (7)
12 Atomiser (7)
14 Plus (4)
16 Arrived by plane (6)
18 Italian sausage (6)
20 Pungent flavour (4)
21 Publicly (7)
24 Utter rapidly (4,3)
25 Oak's fruit (5)
27 Join (metals) (4)
28 Using a pen (7)

DOWN

2 Fury, wrath (3)
3 Second attempt (5)
4 Strain (6)
6 Initial advantage (4,5)
7 NE England river (4)
8 Solidly (7)
9 Historic Spanish fleet (6)
13 Trigger memories (4,1,4)
15 Commiserating with (7)
17 Yellow alcoholic drink (3-3)
19 Money chest (6)
22 Spot on (5)
23 Brag (4)
26 ___ up, confess (3)

Puzzle 66

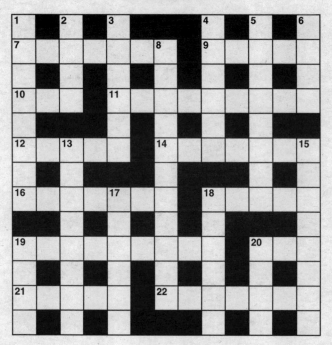

ACROSS

7 Maniacal (7)
9 Solitary type (5)
10 Charged particle (3)
11 Black magic (3,6)
12 Suggest (5)
14 Diabetes treatment (7)
16 Descriptive phrase (7)
18 Enrich with a gift (5)
19 Alertness (9)
20 Chip-shop fish (3)
21 Liking (5)
22 Avidly (7)

DOWN

1 E-number (8)
2 Sign of foreboding (4)
3 Gnarled (6)
4 Idles (6)
5 Straightened (hair) (8)
6 Feel anxious (4)
8 Living in mutual tolerance (2-9)
13 Moralistic (8)
15 In the present (8)
17 Animal lead (6)
18 Vigour (6)
19 Ballot (4)
20 Bottle stopper (4)

Puzzle 67

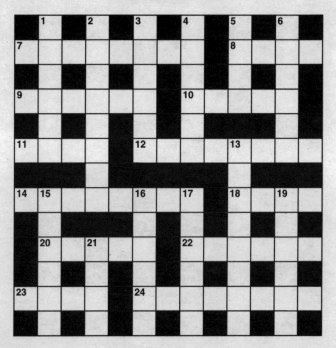

ACROSS

7 Pastry covering (8)
8 Cry (4)
9 Emotionally as one (6)
10 Admit liability (3,2)
11 Beaten instrument (4)
12 Move elsewhere (8)
14 Preach (8)
18 Putrid, fetid (4)
20 One who steals (5)
22 Indistinct, blurred (6)
23 Write your name (4)
24 Lack of manners (8)

DOWN

1 Severity, strictness (6)
2 Scholastic world (8)
3 Kill, slaughter (6)
4 Gentle walk (6)
5 Long-necked bird (4)
6 Clinging mollusc (6)
13 Stimulant found in tea (8)
15 Be too clever for (6)
16 Doddery (6)
17 Personify (6)
19 Discontent (6)
21 Pubs (4)

Puzzle 68

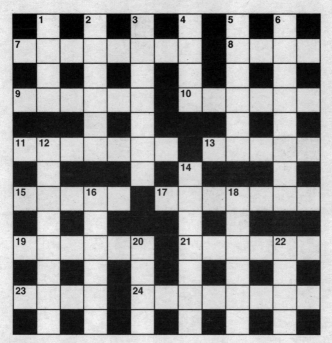

ACROSS

7 Burn slowly (8)
8 Test of knowledge (4)
9 Constant, fixed (6)
10 Smooth and close-fitting (6)
11 Recluses (7)
13 Sound of pain (5)
15 French fries (5)
17 Guardian (7)
19 Not occupied (6)
21 24 times a day (6)
23 Grope, fumble (4)
24 Cheerfulness (8)

DOWN

1 Exude (4)
2 Habit (6)
3 Train (7)
4 Weaponry (4)
5 Nylon grading unit (6)
6 Interest charge (4,4)
12 Intensified (8)
14 Put in a file (7)
16 Tool used with a mortar (6)
18 Origin (6)
20 Symbol of peace (4)
22 Shall we? (4)

Puzzle 69

ACROSS

6 Diabolical (7)
7 Current fashion (5)
9 Blaze (4)
10 Juvenile water-bird (8)
11 Socially acceptable (6)
13 Rinse (4)
15 Pay for (4)
16 Make-believe (6)
18 Dried up by hot weather (3-5)
21 Adjoin (4)
22 Spoil (5)
23 Devotion (7)

DOWN

1 Animal's muzzle (5)
2 Forced into a situation (8)
3 Snow transport (4)
4 Inflamed swelling (4)
5 Equip (7)
8 Goal-getter (6)
12 Brave and determined (6)
13 Erode, whittle down (4,4)
14 Form a line (5,2)
17 Inflicts pain (5)
19 Plain, blunt (4)
20 Entrance to a room (4)

Puzzle 70

ACROSS

1 Speak directly to (7)
5 Yawn (4)
8 Search for water (5)
9 Container for post (7)
11 Go furtively (4)
12 Lift in a hotel (8)
15 A further time (5)
16 Slowing device (5)
19 Callous, brutal (8)
21 Purposes (4)
23 Early evening meal (4,3)
25 To what place? (5)
26 Polluted air (4)
27 Salute by aeroplanes (3-4)

DOWN

2 Utter (9)
3 Stink (4)
4 Comparative phrase (6)
5 Hair goo! (3)
6 Developed picture (5)
7 Peculiarly (5)
10 Turn upside down (6)
13 Embark upon action (4,5)
14 Boneless joint (6)
17 Set upon (6)
18 Residue of a fire (5)
20 Phrase, metaphor (5)
22 Barter (4)
24 Old crone (3)

Puzzle 71

ACROSS

1 Allow into (5)
4 Covered in spots (6)
10 Resort's quiet period (3,6)
11 Peeve (3)
12 Sojourn (5)
13 Slip-ups, blunders (6)
14 Shock, grief (11)
18 Punctual (6)
20 Reference page (5)
23 Debt note (inits) (3)
24 Late news item (4,5)
25 Close (your fist) tightly (6)
26 Ingrained dirt (5)

DOWN

2 Quickly drinks (5)
3 Chilled infusion (4,3)
5 More central (5)
6 In advance of (5,2)
7 Animal harness (4)
8 Covering for the hand (5)
9 Showiness (11)
15 Along the way (2,5)
16 Person on an outing (7)
17 Live (5)
19 Organised sound (5)
21 Reverie (5)
22 Round flat plate (4)

Puzzle 72

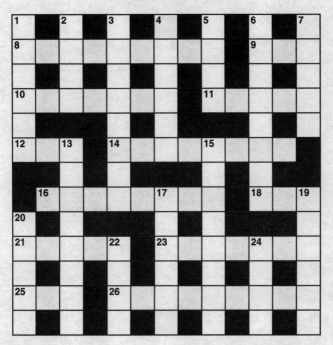

ACROSS

8 Breaks up (9)
9 First number (3)
10 Funny (7)
11 Soft light quilt (5)
12 And so on (abbrev.)(3)
14 Advancing (8)
16 Moisture (8)
18 Until now (3)
21 Luxuriously smooth (5)
23 Supplying (7)
25 Beast of burden (3)
26 Stingers' habitat (5,4)

DOWN

1 Human spirit (6)
2 Tinned meat product (4)
3 Green vegetable (8)
4 Sloping style of writing (6)
5 Pre-owned, second-hand (4)
6 State of having money (8)
7 Small-minded (5)
13 Having no idea (8)
15 Female council chief (8)
17 Stand firm (6)
19 Woman's hosiery item (6)
20 Piece of writing (5)
22 Gape with tiredness (4)
24 Frozen (4)

Puzzle 73

ACROSS

1 Sinister (6)
4 Clean the dishes (4,2)
9 Legal adviser (7)
10 Keep within bounds (5)
11 Release (3,2)
12 Long-armed apes (7)
13 Impetuous and tactless (5)
15 River edges (5)
20 University presentation (7)
22 Communications device (5)
24 Unsavoury broth (5)
25 Stay away from (4,3)
26 Total possessions (6)
27 Plus (2,4)

DOWN

1 Squawk (6)
2 Spew lava (5)
3 Duelling guns (7)
5 Off the cuff (2-3)
6 Poisonous spotted plant (7)
7 Fertilising compound (6)
8 Arrange, straighten (5)
14 Novice (7)
16 Muggy (7)
17 Contagion (6)
18 High points (5)
19 Lamentable (6)
21 Not illuminated (5)
23 Constantly hum (5)

Puzzle 74

ACROSS

1 Dirty look (5)
4 Twitch (5)
10 Desert animal (5)
11 Jungle blade (7)
12 Braids of hair (7)
13 Without fault (5)
14 Impatient (5)
16 Concur (5)
21 Leap (5)
23 Set of straps on a horse (7)
25 Secondary earth layer (7)
26 Fractured (5)
27 Grind your teeth together (5)
28 Totted up (5)

DOWN

2 Make a remark (7)
3 HG ___, author (5)
5 Getting ready for a holiday (7)
6 Beleaguering of a town (5)
7 Sharply pointed (5)
8 Slowly build up (5)
9 Eating occasions (5)
15 Ghastly (7)
17 Unpleasant sight (7)
18 Exploit (5)
19 Will (5)
20 At an oblique angle (5)
22 Of the city (5)
24 Gowned (5)

Puzzle 75

ACROSS

1 Small breed of dog (7)
5 Radioactive (rays) (5)
8 Speed (5)
9 Pellet-filled seat (7)
10 Involved in (5,2)
12 Urge on (5)
14 Cleanse (6)
16 Polar region (6)
18 Ancient artefact (5)
19 Non-religious (7)
22 Gland secretion (7)
24 Noblemen (5)
26 Small and cute (5)
27 Resilient (7)

DOWN

1 Add (3,2)
2 Crash into (3)
3 Satirical sarcasm (5)
4 Decorative strip of cloth (6)
5 Pane-setter (7)
6 Unruly crowd (3)
7 Seraphic (7)
11 Of the country (5)
13 Part of a flower (5)
14 Dry, thirsty (7)
15 Industrial plant (7)
17 Fix the value of (6)
20 Apple-based drink (5)
21 Out of practice (5)
23 Sprint (3)
25 Range of knowledge (3)

Puzzle 76

ACROSS

1 Chit (6)
4 Chaos (6)
8 Going through (3)
9 Off-putting (9)
11 Typical pattern (4)
12 Zodiacal division (4,4)
15 Shy person (9)
18 In the open air (8)
19 Really keen on (4)
21 Inducement (9)
23 Devilish youngster (3)
24 Holy victim (6)
25 Solemn request to God (6)

DOWN

1 Sacred, holy (6)
2 Transport at a skiing resort (9)
3 Noble rank (4)
5 Amplified, expanded (8)
6 Tell fibs (3)
7 Hijack by the crew (6)
10 Fragrant petals (3-6)
13 Become more pronounced (9)
14 Solicitor (8)
16 ___ chloride, common salt (6)
17 Soft brown metal (6)
20 Trepidation (4)
22 Motor vehicle (3)

Puzzle 77

ACROSS

1 Birthday-cake light (6)
4 Fondle, pamper (6)
9 Meteorologist's device (4,5)
10 Purpose (3)
11 Unprocessed metal (3)
12 Gift voucher for a novel? (4,5)
13 Measures of land (5)
15 Grin (5)
20 Ticket there and back (3,6)
22 Try to win the affection of (3)
23 Application (3)
24 Small round pulses (5,4)
25 Struggle roughly (6)
26 Catch out or stumble (4,2)

DOWN

1 Box (for milk) (6)
2 Sound, din (5)
3 Clear enough to read (7)
5 Noticeable (5)
6 Stealthy hunter (7)
7 Using a stopwatch (6)
8 Affect, stage (3,2)
14 Bashful behaviour (7)
16 York ___, cathedral (7)
17 Alter to suit (6)
18 Centres of targets (5)
19 Talk about other people (6)
21 Artist's upright tripod (5)
22 Dog's offspring (5)

Puzzle 78

ACROSS

1 Building's side support (8)
6 Speed contests (5)
7 Which, who or whom (4)
8 Cable-free internet (2-2)
9 Free (of) (3)
10 Coat peg (4)
11 Asian headgear item (6)
13 Excursion (3,3)
14 Rejoinder (6)
17 Milliner's packing (6)
18 Lacking sensation (4)
20 Part of a whistle (3)
21 Requisite (4)
22 In a lazy manner (4)
23 Pain from a nettle (5)
24 Geometrical shape (8)

DOWN

1 Set (of products) (5)
2 Brewing-vessel cover (3,4)
3 Small mistake (4-2)
4 Deride (5)
5 Second-hand vehicle (4,3)
6 Making fun of (7)
12 Housework task (7)
13 Loathe (7)
15 Maimed (7)
16 Extremely (6)
17 Riding garment (5)
19 Consumer (5)

Puzzle 79

ACROSS

1 Aircraft's width (8)
5 Tail of a hare (4)
9 Lay to rest (5)
10 Surgical knife (7)
11 Brewery wagon (4)
12 Wall writings (8)
14 Summon (4,2)
15 Skirt-like beach garment (6)
18 Try-out for actors (8)
20 Measure of distance (4)
22 Electoral division (7)
23 Reverberation (5)
24 Biscuit for baby to chew (4)
25 In the direction of the breeze (8)

DOWN

1 Bizarre (5)
2 Women's team game (7)
3 Gentleman's title (3)
4 Avow (6)
6 1970s Ford model (5)
7 Cultivating (7)
8 Small door for a pet (3,4)
13 Causing harm, cruel (7)
14 Move upwards on all fours (7)
16 Paper-folding art (7)
17 Sound of sobbing (6)
19 Ventures (5)
21 Inched (5)
23 Cheat, defraud (3)

Puzzle 80

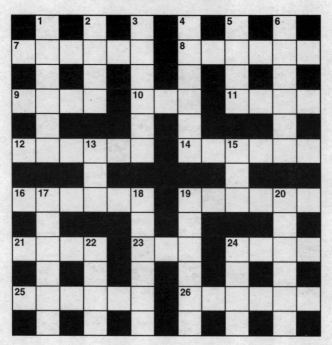

ACROSS

7 One who stalks game (6)
8 Retailer's margin (4-2)
9 Go bananas (4)
10 Worthless horse (3)
11 Sheep's fleece (4)
12 Gummy, tacky (6)
14 Toady, sycophant (3-3)
16 Period of mishaps (3,3)
19 Shingly, stony (6)
21 Falling crystals of ice (4)
23 Stir, fuss (3)
24 Draw near (4)
25 Thick woollen cloth (6)
26 Hostility (6)

DOWN

1 Rent property to another (6)
2 Block (4)
3 Fiery spirit (6)
4 Self-righteously (6)
5 Make (tea or beer) (4)
6 Dawn goddess (6)
13 Chew the ___, ruminate (3)
15 Weep brokenly (3)
17 Spread in many directions (3,3)
18 Per annum (6)
19 Validated (6)
20 Boundaries (6)
22 Drift through the air (4)
24 Nomadic settlement (4)

Puzzle 81

ACROSS

7 Underwater swimmers (6)
8 Eerie (6)
10 Supplemented item (3-2)
11 Of a book, not yet opened (6)
13 Ill-mannered (8)
15 Entreaty (4)
17 Looked at (4)
18 Struggle helplessly (8)
21 Crushed, to make flour (6)
22 Acute apprehension (5)
25 Disconnect from a computer (3,3)
26 Flourish (2,4)

DOWN

1 Portrayed as perfect (9)
2 Fervent (4)
3 Pellet (7)
4 Goads (5)
5 Alleged, ostensible (2-6)
6 PE hall (3)
9 Brusque, snippy (4)
12 Salon fashion? (9)
14 Vegetable parings (8)
16 Rampage (3,4)
19 Youths (4)
20 Hoodwink (5)
23 Leaves (4)
24 Sandwich filling (inits) (3)

Puzzle 82

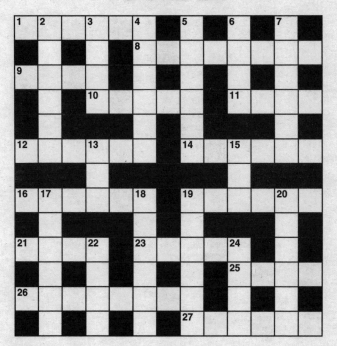

ACROSS

- **1** Spiny-backed lizard (6)
- **8** Twelve old pence (8)
- **9** Mother's mother (4)
- **10** Broad or dense (5)
- **11** Seven days (4)
- **12** Narrow sea lane (6)
- **14** Mummify (6)
- **16** Consumed cigarettes (6)
- **19** Converted into leather (6)
- **21** Crest of a hill (4)
- **23** Spots, stains (5)
- **25** Barren, parched (4)
- **26** Ornamental climbing plant (8)
- **27** On the increase (6)

DOWN

- **2** Artist's attic (6)
- **3** Parent's sister (4)
- **4** Give help (6)
- **5** Unstable (6)
- **6** Travelled by air (4)
- **7** Sick (6)
- **13** Short-winged coastal bird (3)
- **15** Embargo (3)
- **17** Page border (6)
- **18** Prim (6)
- **19** Deposit on the teeth (6)
- **20** Military or naval standard (6)
- **22** Unit of power (4)
- **24** States (4)

Puzzle 83

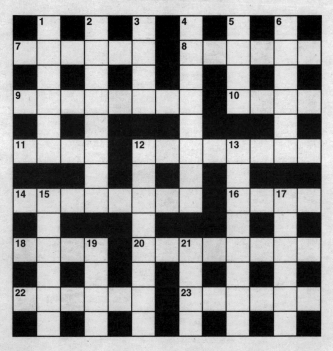

ACROSS

7 Page size (6)
8 Set a tape again (6)
9 Plant used in cosmetics (4,4)
10 Acquire (4)
11 Disengage (4)
12 Photographer's workplace (8)
14 Closure (8)
16 Curved gateway (4)
18 Russia's Ivan, eg (4)
20 Deliberate wrecker (8)
22 Blood product (6)
23 Black magic (6)

DOWN

1 Soft cotton fabric (6)
2 Mail requiring no stamp (8)
3 Small bay (4)
4 Performance test (5,3)
5 Booty (4)
6 Bluish dye (6)
12 Last Judgement (8)
13 Response to a stimulus (8)
15 Persistent annoyance (6)
17 Voucher (6)
19 Other name for iron oxide (4)
21 Posse (4)

Puzzle 84

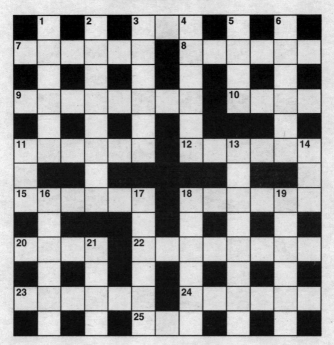

ACROSS

3 Wilt (3)
7 Japanese gown (6)
8 Drilling installation (3,3)
9 Prehistoric (8)
10 Hand weapons (4)
11 Warmth of feeling (6)
12 Get to grips with (6)
15 Ridicule by parodying (4,2)
18 Richly embellished (6)
20 Cut (4)
22 Minor military clash (8)
23 Elongated cream cake (6)
24 Blackmail (6)
25 Affirmative (3)

DOWN

1 Reflective glass (6)
2 ___ Scrubs, prison (8)
3 Crossword puzzler (6)
4 Drinking vessel (6)
5 ___ off, criticise (4)
6 Make an indication (6)
11 Beast of burden (3)
13 Dire misadventure (8)
14 Complete (3)
16 Science of morals (6)
17 Pie case (6)
18 Leads (6)
19 Safeguard (6)
21 Ask earnestly (4)

Puzzle 85

ACROSS

1 Stylish, up-market (6)
4 Mountain's peak (6)
9 ___ up, put into a package (9)
10 Male child (3)
11 Small hotel or pub (3)
12 Two-wheeled vehicle (9)
13 Strait-laced person (5)
15 Played a role (5)
20 Paid a bill (7,2)
22 Chum, mate (3)
23 ___ Baba, panto character (3)
24 Portable laptop computers (9)
25 Powering machine (6)
26 Someone you borrow from (6)

DOWN

1 Trophy game (3-3)
2 Cook's pinny (5)
3 Cooked above boiling water (7)
5 Beneath (5)
6 Pick the wrong moment for (7)
7 Fuel-carrying lorry or ship (6)
8 Piece of material (5)
14 Going bad (7)
16 Competent (7)
17 Get free (6)
18 Amends (proofs) (5)
19 Nearer (to) (6)
21 Bedding items (5)
22 High and mighty (5)

Puzzle 86

ACROSS

1 Advance alerts (8)
6 Pleated frilling (5)
7 Long, limp (of hair) (4)
8 Forbidden (area) (2,2)
9 Alien spacecraft (inits) (3)
10 Back, rear (4)
11 Pail (6)
13 Groups of soldiers (6)
14 Small pebbles (6)
17 Sponsor (6)
18 Move (as a river) (4)
20 Make of cooker (3)
21 Central part of a church (4)
22 Filthy air (4)
23 Carrying out (an action) (5)
24 All together (2,6)

DOWN

1 Celtic language (5)
2 Accidentally met (3,4)
3 Abandon childish ways (4,2)
4 Search (for talent) (5)
5 Spray can (7)
6 Mods' 1960s enemies (7)
12 Adding seasoning (7)
13 In the direction of (7)
15 Large amounts or books (7)
16 Opposite of 'hell' (6)
17 Simple (5)
19 Open railway truck (5)

Puzzle 87

ACROSS

1 Convulsion (5)
4 Prize draw (6)
10 In poor repair (4-5)
11 Mither (3)
12 Attribute (5)
13 Grease tin (6)
14 Noticeable (11)
18 Applicable (6)
20 Gambling game (5)
23 Stage pair (3)
24 Lazy, idle (9)
25 Feign (6)
26 Song of praise (5)

DOWN

2 Variety of bread (5)
3 Doubting Thomas (7)
5 Invalidate (5)
6 Admiring letters (3,4)
7 Irritable (4)
8 Metal worker (5)
9 Relating to the air (11)
15 Die down (4,3)
16 Incentive (7)
17 Non-verse writing (5)
19 Primary (5)
21 Genuflect (5)
22 Concept (4)

Puzzle 88

ACROSS

7 Performing in a play (6)
8 Erase (marks) (3,3)
10 Small prime number (5)
11 Close, sticky (6)
13 Leisure ___, hobbies (8)
15 Suspicious about (2,2)
17 Bishop of Rome (4)
18 Suddenly understood (8)
21 Tiny, small (6)
22 (Had) consumed (5)
25 Keeper, in football (6)
26 Stay awhile (6)

DOWN

1 Drainage tube (5,4)
2 Object in the sky (4)
3 Finally arrived (5,2)
4 Adult or child, person (5)
5 Groups living together (8)
6 Hole in the wall (inits) (3)
9 Person from Glasgow, eg (4)
12 Natives of the UK's capital (9)
14 Exact copies (8)
16 Get up late for work (5,2)
19 On any occasion (4)
20 Room under the roof (5)
23 Roman item of attire (4)
24 Grow old (3)

Puzzle 89

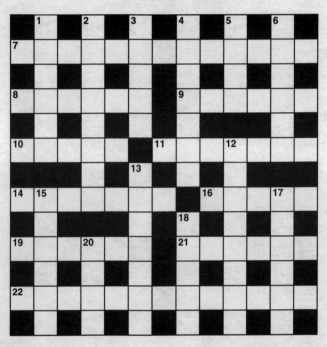

ACROSS

7 Portable seat (8,5)
8 Warm and cosy (fabric) (6)
9 Switch on a radio (4,2)
10 Sag (5)
11 Worship, ritual (7)
14 Wages for ill employees (4,3)
16 Order issued by a lawgiver (5)
19 Provide, give (6)
21 Straighten out (6)
22 Unfeasible (13)

DOWN

1 Harpooners' boat (6)
2 Tugged piece of hair? (8)
3 Plastic used for LPs (5)
4 Selfish morale boost (3,4)
5 Astonish (4)
6 Causing a dull pain (6)
12 Making progress (5,3)
13 Enclosed field (7)
15 Evil reputation (6)
17 Icily (6)
18 Learner at school (5)
20 Belonging to you and me (4)

Puzzle 90

ACROSS

1 Seize (power) by force (5)
4 Steak (1-4)
10 Without much space (7)
11 Film crowd-filler (5)
12 Decorated with sugar (4)
13 Start a voyage (3,2,3)
16 Equable (6)
17 Violently cross a border (6)
20 Sponsored baby at baptism (8)
21 Reeded instrument (4)
23 Search, rummage (5)
25 Ornamental fish (3,4)
26 Terrible pain (5)
27 Small forests (5)

DOWN

2 Theatre worker (9)
3 Spellbound (4)
5 Complaining (8)
6 Bolt's counterpart (3)
7 Economise severely (6)
8 Find the total of (3,2)
9 Volcanic matter (4)
14 Right-hand side at sea (9)
15 Age of majority (8)
18 Absolve (6)
19 Accidental success (5)
20 Clothes (4)
22 Fodder store (4)
24 Multi-seeded fruit (3)

Puzzle 91

ACROSS

8 Do-or-die (4-5)
9 In time past (3)
10 Orchestral instrument (5)
11 Allowing to borrow (7)
12 Image consultant (7)
13 Adept (4)
17 Racing probability (4)
18 Deep-fat fryer (4,3)
22 Fell (7)
24 Non-reacting (5)
25 Grandma (3)
26 Doing magic tricks (9)

DOWN

1 Section of garlic (5)
2 Variegated, mixed (8)
3 In a perfect world (7)
4 Props for walking tall (6)
5 Flour grain (5)
6 Indian woman's dress (4)
7 Skier's glasses (7)
14 Dare (2,1,5)
15 Dwellings (7)
16 Best possible (7)
19 Concealing (6)
20 Small spot (5)
21 Platform for performing (5)
23 Hostelries (4)

Puzzle 92

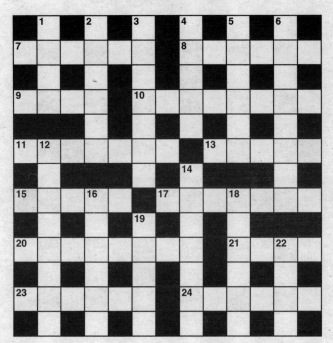

ACROSS

7 Horse noise (6)
8 Permeable by liquids (6)
9 Nothing, nil (4)
10 Military quarters (8)
11 Cordially (7)
13 Synthetic fibre (5)
15 Guts, spirit (5)
17 Exotic flowers (7)
20 Scruffy (book) (3-5)
21 Variety (4)
23 Prepared and heated food (6)
24 Beating with a rod (6)

DOWN

1 Brogue, loafer, eg (4)
2 Expensive wool (6)
3 Visual organ (7)
4 Separate (5)
5 Old and stiff (6)
6 Burgers, fries etc (4,4)
12 Be forced to bat again (6,2)
14 Ship-repair station (3,4)
16 Impertinent (6)
18 Holidaying on foot (6)
19 New wife (5)
22 Number of skittle pins (4)

Puzzle 93

ACROSS

1 Not hindered (12)
9 Stiff (5)
10 Lack of movement (7)
11 Restrain (8)
12 Symbol on a stave (4)
14 Relaxed (2,4)
15 For adult viewing (1-5)
18 Adult kid (4)
20 Demonstration house (4,4)
23 Urban (area) (5-2)
24 Brisk (5)
25 Dubious account (1,6,5)

DOWN

2 Bed dress (7)
3 One seeking nirvana (8)
4 Meagrely (6)
5 Manipulated (4)
6 Entirety (5)
7 Towered over (7)
8 Finished level (4)
13 Common rodent (5,3)
14 Field of mathematics (7)
16 Very reliable person (7)
17 Rough (sea) (6)
19 Courtroom plea of elsewhere (5)
21 Gentle whirlpool (4)
22 Eye infection (4)

Puzzle 94

ACROSS

1 Tuxedo (6,6)
9 Warp (7)
10 Coating (5)
11 Pour down (4)
12 In the vicinity (7)
15 Decree (6)
16 Degenerate (6)
19 View (7)
21 Disregard (4)
24 Welsh breed of dog (5)
25 Dog of mixed breed (7)
26 Farm-worker's dish? (9,3)

DOWN

2 Alternatively (7)
3 Cosy niche (4)
4 Give up work (6)
5 Hint (8)
6 Enter data (3,2)
7 Grassy surface (4)
8 Issue (7)
13 Diabolically wicked (8)
14 Fit (7)
17 Old Japanese warrior (7)
18 Past (6)
20 Money bag (5)
22 Divisions of a play (4)
23 Nest-making insects (4)

Puzzle 95

ACROSS

1 Bow-legged (5)
4 Undress (7)
9 Took to the streets (8)
10 Small restaurant (4)
11 Overindulge (6)
12 Social outcast (6)
13 Map indication? (1,5,3,4)
17 Knotty (6)
19 Turn down (6)
21 Floating waste matter (4)
22 Persona (8)
23 Mitigate, relieve (7)
24 Woodland sprite (5)

DOWN

2 Boxing ring (5)
3 Eye-medicine dispenser (7)
5 Extensively (2,5)
6 Crop up again (5)
7 Large horned wild ox (7)
8 Begin to move (4)
14 Percussion instruments (7)
15 Tailoring (7)
16 Teddy bear, eg (4,3)
18 Welsh name for Wales (5)
19 Oboe's mouthpiece (4)
20 Start (a business) (3,2)

Puzzle 96

ACROSS

1 (Look) with disdain (7)
4 Cram for exams (4)
9 Error (7)
11 Put your name forward (5)
12 Fourth Greek letter (5)
13 Academy (6)
15 Conventional, standard (6)
17 Take by force (6)
19 Spanish rice dish (6)
20 Teenage groups (5)
23 Carried by the wind (5)
24 Energetic (7)
25 Walrus' long tooth (4)
26 Interesting incident (7)

DOWN

2 Bone encasing the brain (5)
3 Bob (to royalty) (6)
5 Completely obliterate (4,3)
6 Children's playthings (4)
7 ___ by, complying with (7)
8 AK-47, eg (7,3)
10 Fail to elicit any result (4,1,5)
14 One of the sciences (7)
16 Uses logic (7)
18 Settled the bill (4,2)
21 Desert traveller (5)
22 Encourage to do wrong (4)

Puzzle 97

ACROSS

1 Minor setback (6)
4 Photograph of a celebrity (3-2)
8 Frenzy (5)
9 Upmarket (product) (4-3)
10 Wreath of flowers (7)
11 Song of praise (4)
12 Churchyard tree (3)
14 Chimney (4)
15 Restless desire (4)
18 Gene code (inits) (3)
21 Dislodge (4)
23 Free from pretence (7)
25 Distorted (sound) (7)
26 Nude, unclothed (5)
27 Just, proper (5)
28 (Lead) into trouble (6)

DOWN

1 Respect, tribute (6)
2 Hold the reins (7)
3 Without let-up (8)
4 ___ stick, bouncy toy (4)
5 Deprived (5)
6 Stickler for detail (6)
7 Legally questionable (5)
13 Prize money (8)
16 Examiner (7)
17 Maker of fake money (6)
19 Stage whisper (5)
20 Period of vigour (6)
22 Flower bunch (5)
24 Lump (of cream) (4)

Puzzle 98

ACROSS

7 Style of tennis shot (8)
8 Actual (4)
10 Bet win and place (4-3)
11 Blowy (5)
12 Mr Punch's dog (4)
13 Oozing (7)
16 Assign (7)
18 Pat (of butter) (4)
22 Newly married man (5)
24 Mischievous sprite (7)
25 Void (4)
26 Memento (8)

DOWN

1 Miserable, woeful (6)
2 Drinks coolers (3,5)
3 Flamboyant (5)
4 Biochemical catalyst (6)
5 Wartime woman sailor (4)
6 Blue-green gem (5)
9 Nick, pinch (5)
14 Lanky (8)
15 Metric weights (5)
17 Largest foot digit (3,3)
19 Relating to two, in computing (6)
20 Person acting for another (5)
21 Dish up (food) (5)
23 Exclusively (4)

Puzzle 99

ACROSS

7 Frozen treat (4-3)
8 Artery of the heart (5)
9 Sink (a snooker ball) (3)
10 Battledress colour (5)
11 Leap on one leg (3)
12 Footprints (6)
14 Artist's workroom (6)
16 Hidden, dormant (6)
17 Gardener's hand tool (6)
19 Betting suggestion (3)
21 Make amends (for) (5)
23 Chapel bench (3)
24 Beat (5)
25 Stalker (7)

DOWN

1 Written agreement (8)
2 Cow's yield (4)
3 Nut variety (5)
4 Container for film stock (8)
5 Curve (4)
6 Hanger-on (4-8)
7 Giving in (12)
13 Australian marsupial (8)
15 Heavy rainfall (8)
18 Circus jumping rings (5)
20 Household animals (4)
22 Spikes (of corn) (4)

Puzzle 100

ACROSS

1 Self-consciously (5)
4 ___ Night, January 6 (7)
9 Fragrant, scented (8)
10 Seductive woman (4)
11 Pub bar (6)
12 Within a house (6)
13 Pastoral (6)
16 Large rich cake (6)
18 Any individual (6)
20 Although (6)
22 Brainwave (4)
23 Frozen confection (3,5)
24 Unbending (7)
25 Michaelmas daisy (5)

DOWN

2 'Laughing' carnivore (5)
3 Excluded (4,3)
5 Marriage ceremony (7)
6 Cherished (5)
7 Lottery at a fair (7)
8 Forewarning (4)
14 Inverted (2-5)
15 Send, ship (7)
17 Men's outfitters (7)
19 Mass (5)
20 Unwanted plant (4)
21 Ointment (5)

Puzzle 101

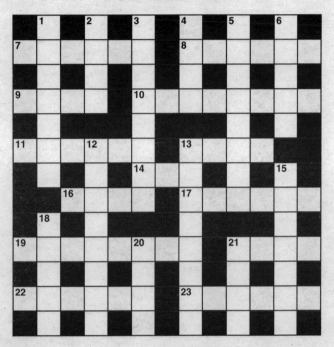

ACROSS

7 Battered prawns (6)
8 Room for storing food (6)
9 Herb served with lamb (4)
10 Pardoning, letting off (8)
11 Two-way sound system (6)
13 Trip to visit places (4)
14 Contents of a balloon (3)
16 Outline of a story (4)
17 Tree-lined road (6)
19 Style of blinds (8)
21 Precious red jewel (4)
22 Shrink back in fear (6)
23 Send goods abroad (6)

DOWN

1 Written copies (of shows) (7)
2 Give off (fumes) (4)
3 Coastal rescue vessel (8)
4 Smart ___, know-all (4)
5 ___ cooker, kitchen item (8)
6 Long-running kids' comic (5)
12 Giving an account of (8)
13 New recruits (8)
15 Erasers (7)
18 Great haste or urgency (5)
20 Covered (a cake) (4)
21 Ready to be harvested (4)

Puzzle 102

ACROSS

6 Body parts to pierce (3,5)
8 Suspended (4)
10 Upper part of the leg (5)
11 Stop (6)
13 Lines of light (4)
14 Crowing, boasting (8)
16 Behind the scenes (3-5)
19 Junk electronic mail (4)
22 Covered with blooms (6)
23 Adherent of Wicca (5)
25 Weight of responsibility (4)
26 Keeper's zone in soccer (4,4)

DOWN

1 Unaffected by great warmth (9)
2 Rich pungent coffee (5)
3 Patch up (6)
4 Breakfast cereal (6)
5 Item laid by a reptile (3)
7 Showery (5)
9 Lees, sediment (5)
12 Narcissist (9)
15 Stockpile (5)
17 Restock, replenish (4,2)
18 Eight pints (6)
20 Bleeper (5)
21 Overflow (5)
24 Happiness (3)

Puzzle 103

ACROSS

1 Protect (a weapon) (7)
5 Froth on the sea (5)
9 Feel anxious (4)
10 Death (8)
11 Mechanical man (5)
12 Sons of kings (7)
14 Not sporting (6)
16 Calm, appease (6)
18 Write or telephone (7)
20 Custom, practice (5)
22 Yielded to temptation (8)
24 Metal liable to rust (4)
25 Disparaging (remark) (5)
26 Sweet and sickly (7)

DOWN

2 Whaling spear (7)
3 Space traveller (9)
4 Fit of annoyance (4)
6 Friend, mate (3)
7 Bishop's head-dress (5)
8 Mix (4,2)
13 Prerequisite (9)
15 Contemporary (6)
17 Nautical warning device (7)
19 Pacific, for example (5)
21 Much-loved actor (4)
23 Goat's young (3)

Puzzle 104

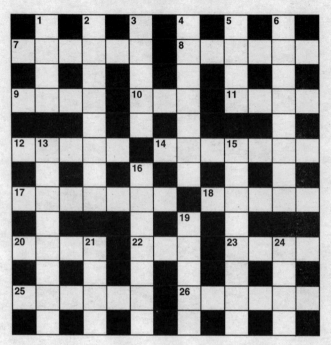

ACROSS

7 Town just north of Windsor (6)
8 Paraphrase (6)
9 Tinted (4)
10 French word for 'water' (3)
11 Sends out shoots (4)
12 Vacuum ___, thermos (5)
14 Fabric of sheer silk (7)
17 Clairvoyant, medium (7)
18 Spry (5)
20 Exhale sharply (4)
22 Inner Hebrides isle (3)
23 Melody, air (4)
25 OT hymns (6)
26 Relinquish or yield (4,2)

DOWN

1 Remove the skin from (4)
2 Dead end (3-2-3)
3 Horse's footplates (5)
4 Cantankerous (7)
5 Absorbent cotton pad (4)
6 Unrefined fuel (5,3)
13 Having little energy (8)
15 Escapee (8)
16 Stray from the point (7)
19 Reflection (in a mirror) (5)
21 Saunter (4)
24 Naming part of speech (4)

Puzzle 105

ACROSS

1 Visualising (6)
5 Manage (4)
8 Medieval armour material (5,4)
9 Be sorry for (3)
11 Functions (4)
12 Legendary lover (8)
14 Slowly get into the mind (6)
16 Protective hat (6)
18 Due to arrive (8)
19 Constituent of brass (4)
22 Flightless bird (3)
23 Murderer (3-6)
24 Additional tax (4)
25 Religious crime (6)

DOWN

2 Escape from (5)
3 Public houses (4)
4 Shoo! (2,4)
5 Accosted (8)
6 Enact (7)
7 Examine closely (10)
10 Springiness (10)
13 Worthless, trivial (8)
15 Isolate (7)
17 Informer (6)
20 Golf clubs (5)
21 Scorch (4)

Puzzle 106

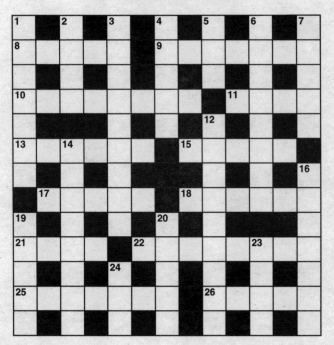

ACROSS

8 Up to the time of (5)
9 Storehouse for weapons (7)
10 Fellow employee (8)
11 Unconscious state (4)
13 Site, venue (6)
15 Rebuff (5)
17 Expressionless (5)
18 Powerless aircraft (6)
21 Too, as well (4)
22 Self-rule (8)
25 River crossings (7)
26 Encourage (3,2)

DOWN

1 Go out of control (3,4)
2 Media hero (4)
3 Aid for finding the vertical (5,4)
4 Unwanted material (5)
5 Mischievous sprite (3)
6 Based on hearsay (8)
7 Minor road (5)
12 Unexpected consequence (9)
14 Nubuck (8)
16 Entreating (7)
19 Sheep's babies (5)
20 Ward worker (5)
23 Excessive indulgence (4)
24 Grow old (3)

Puzzle 107

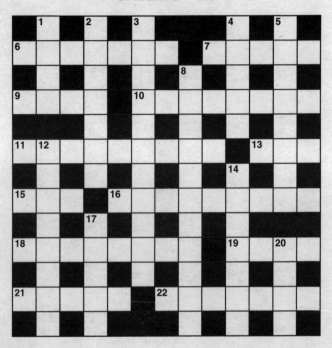

ACROSS

6 Artillery soldiers (7)
7 Tartan (5)
9 Settee, couch (4)
10 Trouble (8)
11 Inform on someone (4,5)
13 Young seal (3)
15 Wordplay (3)
16 Harlots (9)
18 Motorway entrance (4,4)
19 Convent sisters (4)
21 Feed with fuel (5)
22 Put inside (7)

DOWN

1 Japanese wrestling (4)
2 Sissy, wimpish (7)
3 Deal (11)
4 Regard smugly (5)
5 Reduce the price of (8)
8 Dairy dessert (4,7)
12 Fairness (8)
14 Lanky (7)
17 Barbed (5)
20 Snout (4)

Puzzle 108

ACROSS

1 Hurling (8)
5 Hare's tail (4)
8 Non-criminal legislation (5,3)
9 Speak sharply (4)
11 Male sweetheart (4)
12 Simmer down (4,3)
14 On all sides (6)
16 Sharp-tasting (6)
18 Prosper (7)
19 Chiropodist's interest (4)
22 Double-reed instrument (4)
23 Monotony (8)
24 Powdery earth (4)
25 Naively credulous (4-4)

DOWN

1 Mexican snack (4)
2 Theatrical show (5)
3 Determination (10)
4 Hint, suggestion (6)
6 State of agreement (7)
7 Font (8)
10 In an assertive manner (10)
13 Hard feelings (3,5)
15 Smelly (7)
17 Tarnished (6)
20 Mourning poem (5)
21 Far from brand-new (4)

Puzzle 109

ACROSS

1 Property dealer (6,5)
8 Strategy, plan (6)
9 One of five on each hand (6)
10 Arch used in croquet (4)
11 Rebuke, upbraiding (8)
13 Phrases (5)
15 Physical game (5)
18 Secret user ID (8)
19 Spiral (4)
20 Central American country (6)
21 View, watch (4,2)
22 Legal enforcement (3,3,5)

DOWN

2 TV drama serial (4,5)
3 Misbehave (3,2)
4 Scramble (text) (6)
5 Laugh (6)
6 Of paint, less runny (3-4)
7 For nothing (4)
12 Block, obstruct (9)
14 Eye make-up (7)
16 Moonlight ___, piano piece (6)
17 Putrid (egg) (6)
18 Hose (4)
19 Company of singers (5)

Puzzle 110

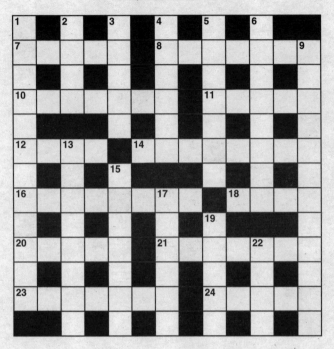

ACROSS

7 Put on the scales (5)
8 Irregular (7)
10 Enforce (laws) (3,4)
11 Between Heaven and Hell (5)
12 Band of criminals (4)
14 Microscopic organisms (8)
16 Laboratory cylinder (4,4)
18 Against (4)
20 Directive (5)
21 Straighten (7)
23 Begrudging (7)
24 Abbot's subordinate (5)

DOWN

1 Run-down urban area (8,4)
2 Large fragrant flower (4)
3 Filming session (5)
4 ___ pig, rodent (6)
5 Characteristic (7)
6 Try-out (5,3)
9 Be beautiful (4,1,7)
13 Plunge, plummet (8)
15 Eminence (7)
17 Skin contusion (6)
19 Phases (5)
22 Part of the eye (4)

Puzzle 111

ACROSS

7 Acting timidly (12)
9 Track down (4,3)
10 Horned pachyderm (5)
11 React in surprise (4)
12 From the start (3,5)
14 Oktoberfest marquee (4,4)
17 Earnest student (4)
20 Lift up, praise highly (5)
21 Expanded (7)
23 Instant, reflex (12)

DOWN

1 Impersonates (4)
2 Respect (6)
3 Power cable support (5)
4 Lodging place (6)
5 For always (7)
6 Very dark blue pigment (6)
8 Fail to recollect (6)
11 Prate (6)
13 Variety of cheese (7)
15 Range (6)
16 Naked lifestyle (6)
18 Thin, runny (6)
19 Open space in a wood (5)
22 Fathers (4)

Puzzle 112

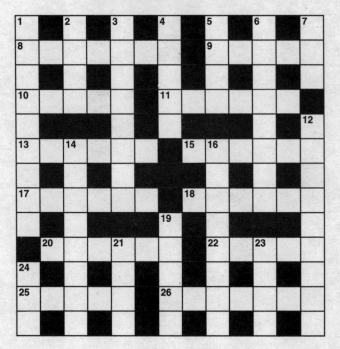

ACROSS

8 Tedious (7)
9 Musical play (5)
10 Sorcery (5)
11 Chinese martial art (4,2)
13 Ungainly walk (6)
15 Get fond of (4,2)
17 Uncomprehending (6)
18 Large lavish (meal) (4-2)
20 Venomous creatures (6)
22 Electricity supply (5)
25 Domineering (5)
26 Spellbind (7)

DOWN

1 Colour-changing African lizard (9)
2 Pleased with yourself! (4)
3 Elegant, tasteful (8)
4 Full of fumes (5)
5 Cut down (4)
6 Resourcefulness (4-4)
7 Candle substance (3)
12 Work in conjunction (2-7)
14 Delay (8)
16 Jamaica pepper (8)
19 Small bits of land (5)
21 Door lockers (4)
23 Lash mark (4)
24 Backward flow (3)

Puzzle 113

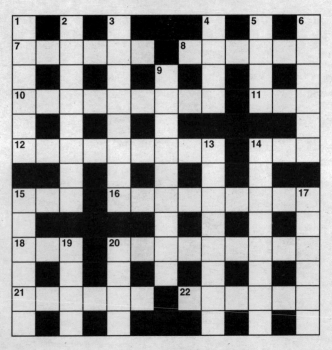

ACROSS

7 Fountainhead (6)
8 Meekly, modestly (6)
10 Jettison (3,4,2)
11 Intense desire (3)
12 Profane (9)
14 ___ for, decide on (3)
15 Cease to be (3)
16 Stationery item (9)
18 Weep loudly (3)
20 Stage speech for one (9)
21 Release from a coiled state (6)
22 Salted snack (6)

DOWN

1 Counterfeit (6)
2 Aversion (8)
3 Drink taken before bed (8)
4 Lawn surface (4)
5 Deftly (4)
6 Baby swan (6)
9 Taping up (9)
13 Signed on (8)
14 Ready to help (8)
15 Serve (food) (4,2)
17 Good supply (6)
19 Basin (4)
20 Weasel-like animal (4)

Puzzle 114

ACROSS

1 Highland Games pole (5)
4 Technical expertise (4-3)
8 Study of living things (7)
9 Colour of old photos (5)
10 Reminder (4)
11 Design of window (3)
12 Hindu mystic (4)
15 Obstruct (a process) (6)
16 Small short-haired canine (3,3)
19 Central cathedral section (4)
21 Amusement (3)
22 Tinted (4)
26 Food from Heaven (5)
27 Sinful (7)
28 Phoning, ringing (7)
29 Liable to droop (5)

DOWN

1 Lodge made from logs (5)
2 Partially dried herring (7)
3 Underground stem (4)
4 Set of buttons to press (6)
5 Evict (4)
6 Large, herbivorous African mammal (5)
7 Cloth-making on a loom (7)
13 Fruit that is sometimes dried (3)
14 Junior Scout (3)
15 Energetic, forceful (7)
17 Continuing from dawn till dusk (3-4)
18 Official decision made in a court (6)
20 Record-making material (5)
23 Powdery (5)
24 Hired car and driver (4)
25 Imitates (4)

Puzzle 115

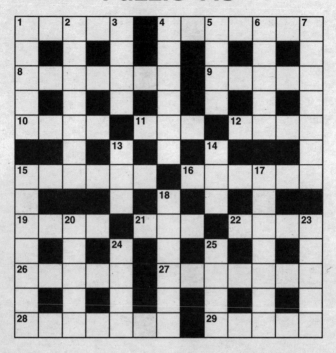

ACROSS

1 Coated, encrusted (5)
4 Event with a 'best of breed' competition (3,4)
8 Part of a rocket's equipment (7)
9 Solitary person (5)
10 Castle chess piece (4)
11 Perform on stage (3)
12 Strong Turkish spirit (4)
15 Puffs up (6)
16 Nonsense, or a striped sweet (6)
19 Give a title to (4)
21 Sporting trophy (3)
22 Toss (a coin in the air) (4)
26 Was the proprietor of (5)
27 First-aid accessory (3,4)
28 Front limb (7)
29 Clause added to a document (5)

DOWN

1 Pickled bud used in sauces (5)
2 Slot in a door (7)
3 Steep decline (4)
4 Subtract (6)
5 Cheek, impudence (4)
6 Red hair-dye (5)
7 In running order (7)
13 Viral infection (3)
14 Make an incision (3)
15 Ventilating panel on top of a car (7)
17 Short concrete post (7)
18 Seething (6)
20 Person under age (5)
23 Gambling game (5)
24 Man-made god (4)
25 Show signs of age (4)

Puzzle 116

ACROSS

- **1** Not justified (11)
- **9** ___ Gras, Shrove Tuesday carnival (5)
- **10** Piece of permanent equipment (7)
- **11** Advancing (money) (7)
- **12** Make changes to (5)
- **13** Speed and rhythm (5)
- **15** Particle of snow (5)
- **20** Bohemian dance (5)
- **22** Beats, pounds (7)
- **24** How come? (4,3)
- **25** Third letter of the Greek alphabet (5)
- **26** Understand a clock (4,3,4)

DOWN

- **2** Recount (7)
- **3** Defendant's whereabouts claim (5)
- **4** Safe house (6)
- **5** Women's team game (7)
- **6** Build (5)
- **7** Move at an easy pace (5)
- **8** Sharply evident (5)
- **14** Jokey (7)
- **16** Don't say a word (4,3)
- **17** Mass of eggs (5)
- **18** Building with an altar (6)
- **19** Written composition (5)
- **21** Military time off (5)
- **23** Power (5)

Puzzle 117

ACROSS

1 Impassive, expressionless (7)
5 Piece of medicated cotton for cleaning a wound (4)
10 Devout, godly (5)
11 Uniformly (7)
12 Quick, vigorous massage (3,4)
14 Small cut or groove (4)
16 Practically, approximately (6)
18 Eastern marketplace (6)
20 Floating waste (4)
21 Not as heavy (7)
24 Secret planner (7)
25 Narrow-minded, intolerant person (5)
27 Ballet dancer's skirt (4)
28 Poor (weather conditions) (7)

DOWN

2 One's self-esteem (3)
3 Club for dancing (5)
4 Maturing (6)
6 Information source in a classroom (4-5)
7 Male children (4)
8 Economical (7)
9 Old currency unit, worth £1.05 (6)
13 Diversify (6,3)
15 Commensurate (3,4)
17 Boundaries (6)
19 Ignited suddenly (6)
22 Roof support wall (5)
23 Petty quarrel, tiff (4)
26 Fuel used for cooking (3)

Puzzle 118

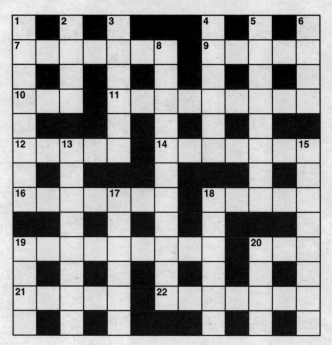

ACROSS

7 Sports game that is played again (7)
9 Occasion (5)
10 Made a hole in soil (3)
11 Scene of park concerts (9)
12 Pizza-topping fruit (5)
14 Pastoral (7)
16 Tactile (7)
18 Garment similar to a bolero (5)
19 Having a lot of space (9)
20 Lie (3)
21 Parts of sentences made up of syllables (5)
22 Person with a vote (7)

DOWN

1 Compromise exchange (5-3)
2 Pleased with yourself! (4)
3 Unlikely to move or change (6)
4 Forceful, determined (6)
5 Seller of high-street goods (8)
6 Breeding farm (4)
8 On intimate terms (4,2,5)
13 Lacking competence (8)
15 Canary or budgie, eg (4,4)
17 Make a surgical cut (6)
18 Nurse or nun (6)
19 Monk's hood (4)
20 Foods such as butter and lard (4)

Puzzle 119

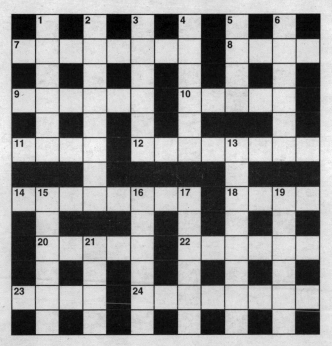

ACROSS

7 Loosen muscles (6,2)
8 Arranged (4)
9 Admit as a member (6)
10 Nude, unclothed (5)
11 Prepare for publication (4)
12 Fact verifiers (8)
14 First-class, excellent (4,4)
18 Point of the compass (4)
20 Bungle (your lines in a play) (5)
22 Pervaded (6)
23 Substance which turns litmus paper red (4)
24 Leading astray (8)

DOWN

1 Preserved in a metal container (6)
2 Brusquely (8)
3 Area round the North Pole (6)
4 Victoria ___, cake (6)
5 Anti-aircraft fire (4)
6 More ferocious (6)
13 Withhold (4,4)
15 Result, impression (6)
16 Lacking harmony (3-3)
17 Exquisite, charming (6)
19 Spotting (6)
21 Disengage (4)

Puzzle 120

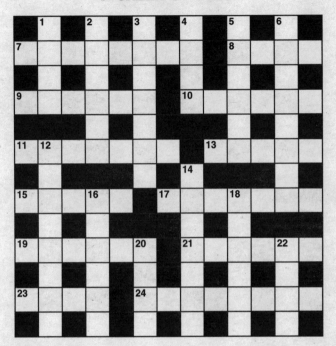

ACROSS

7 Buildings, or hypotheses (8)
8 Measure of nautical speed (4)
9 Plain cotton fabric (6)
10 Countermand (6)
11 Assuage (7)
13 Tall metal structure for electricity cables (5)
15 Unpleasant facial expression (5)
17 Wiry, sinewy (7)
19 Preserved, cured (6)
21 Likeness of a person (6)
23 Incinerate (4)
24 Dawn sound (4,4)

DOWN

1 Accompanied vocal solo in an opera (4)
2 Have a drink (6)
3 Support (a cause) (7)
4 Russian ruler (4)
5 Maid-of-all-work (6)
6 Traditional ballad or ditty (4,4)
12 Reviving beverage (4-2-2)
14 In reality, deep down (2,5)
16 Arousing (6)
18 Contaminate (6)
20 Amount due (4)
22 Force 8 wind (4)

Puzzle 121

ACROSS

1 Hardly known (7)
5 Droplet-shaped fruit (4)
8 Lifting gear (5)
9 Flour-makers (7)
11 Large drainage channel (4)
12 Washbasin fitting (5,3)
15 Sweeping implement (5)
16 Boulder-strewn (5)
19 Insectivorous spiny mammal (8)
21 Hare's tail (4)
23 Rear limb (4,3)
25 Cherished (5)
26 Keep under hatches (4)
27 Bread variety (7)

DOWN

2 Narrow-minded (9)
3 Felines (4)
4 Continue to be in the same condition (6)
5 Friend, mate (3)
6 Major blood vessel (5)
7 Of dubious character (5)
10 Keep out of sight, go to ground (3,3)
13 Find shelter (4,5)
14 Succeed (2,4)
17 Person who cuts down trees for a living (6)
18 Pore over books (5)
20 Order issued by a lawgiver (5)
22 Layout (4)
24 Water formed by condensation at night (3)

Puzzle 122

ACROSS

1 Momentary gleam of light (5)
4 Deteriorate, decline (6)
10 Human target (6,3)
11 Nautical journal (3)
12 Trim, spruce (5)
13 Fish-eating bird of prey (6)
14 Truce (5,6)
18 Wild dog-like animal (6)
20 Verve (5)
23 No longer alight, extinguished (3)
24 Make less strong or intense (5,4)
25 Youthful-looking (6)
26 Third gift of the Magi (5)

DOWN

2 Immature insect (5)
3 Doubting person (7)
5 Admit (3,2)
6 Striking (7)
7 Keeps pestering (4)
8 Break to bits (5)
9 Life in perpetuity (11)
15 With precision (7)
16 Ardently (7)
17 Discovered (5)
19 New Zealanders (5)
21 Look high and low (5)
22 Mausoleum (4)

Puzzle 123

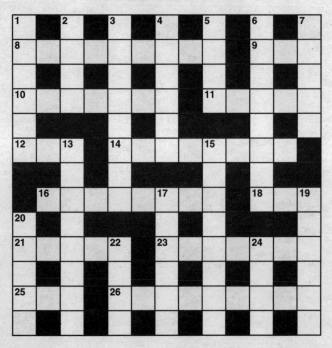

ACROSS

8 Procured dishonestly (3-6)
9 Promissory note (inits) (3)
10 Pupil (7)
11 Follow on (5)
12 Gentle knock (3)
14 Game also known as soccer (8)
16 Degenerate (2,2,4)
18 Ogee shape (3)
21 Colour of envy (5)
23 Sincerity, frankness (7)
25 Central issue at the core of a problem (3)
26 Scientific study of legends (9)

DOWN

1 Sow's baby (6)
2 Entreaty (4)
3 (Pace) repetitively (2,3,3)
4 Twin sound system (6)
5 A single time (4)
6 Mouth balm (3-5)
7 Preserved as by salting (5)
13 Sayings, maxims (8)
15 Thanks to, via (2,4,2)
17 Rouse, stimulate (6)
19 Decorative bunches of leaves or flowers (6)
20 Person authorised to do business for another (5)
22 Unfeeling (4)
24 Slender wind instrument (4)

Puzzle 124

ACROSS

1 Whim, capricious idea (5)
4 Urge (3,2)
10 Flower grown in Holland (5)
11 Fingerless gloves (7)
12 Definite (7)
13 Foolish (5)
14 Restless, fidgety (5)
16 One more time (5)
21 Luxuriate (in) (5)
23 Damsels (7)
25 Rouse (7)
26 Surrounding of a town (5)
27 Lightly fried (potatoes) (5)
28 Level of development (5)

DOWN

2 Physical complaint (7)
3 ___ pants, tapered cropped women's trousers (5)
5 Acquiring (7)
6 Musical drama such as *Carmen* (5)
7 Small ladder (5)
8 Firmly fix (5)
9 Willow for basket-making (5)
15 Lend a hand (4,3)
17 Variety of lettuce (7)
18 Complaint, point of dissatisfaction (5)
19 Force (5)
20 Court official (5)
22 Stringed instrument (5)
24 Added small photo (5)

Puzzle 125

ACROSS

1 Therapist who kneads parts of the body (7)
5 Group of singers (5)
8 Dramatic performer (5)
9 Competent (7)
10 Wild pig with large tusks (7)
12 Place for newly arrived emails (5)
14 Thickset (6)
16 Bringer of news (6)
18 Body of salt water (5)
19 Jittery, on edge (7)
22 One whose job is raising animals (7)
24 Legally adequate (5)
26 Popular card game (5)
27 Medieval punishment frame (7)

DOWN

1 Cat's sound (5)
2 Pose for an artist (3)
3 One of the ancient elements (5)
4 Concede defeat (6)
5 Food, cooking (7)
6 Cancelled (3)
7 At ease (7)
11 Wake up right by the river (5)
13 Cry of approval (5)
14 Dribble (7)
15 Completely desiccated (4-3)
17 Catch in a snare (6)
20 Adversary (5)
21 In a forlorn way (5)
23 'Dutch disease' tree (3)
25 Fifth sign of the zodiac (3)

Puzzle 126

ACROSS

1 Block on which to place a statue (6)
4 Atlas Mountains' continent (6)
8 And so forth (abbrev.)(3)
9 Replace, discard (9)
11 Identifying symbol (4)
12 Guiding (a car) (8)
15 Launch (9)
18 Mathematics of shapes (8)
19 Second part of a triple jump (4)
21 Hypodermic procedure (9)
23 Drink taken with milk or lemon (3)
24 Early stage of reproduction (6)
25 Sculptor's tool (6)

DOWN

1 Spanish rice dish (6)
2 Under a false name (9)
3 Job of work (4)
5 Aggressive (8)
6 Wrath, rage (3)
7 Take retribution for (6)
10 Dried petals for perfuming a room (3-6)
13 Boots with blades (3,6)
14 Rubbery (8)
16 Catch fire (6)
17 Extend untidily (of a city) (6)
20 Small measurement of length (4)
22 Poke sharply (3)

Puzzle 127

ACROSS

1 Arm muscle (6)
4 Type of printing (6)
9 Method of photographing long slow processes (4-5)
10 Personal manner (3)
11 Non-scientific subject (3)
12 Fluctuating (2,3,4)
13 Church with a convent (5)
15 Nation (5)
20 Plastic headgear item for bathing (6,3)
22 Violin string material (3)
23 Archaic measurement of length (3)
24 Costing next to nothing (4,5)
25 Sickly sweet (6)
26 More humid (6)

DOWN

1 Officer's attendant (6)
2 Heavenly body with a luminous tail (5)
3 Make foul or impure (7)
5 Meadow (5)
6 Harbour for large ships (7)
7 Wearying (6)
8 Use an aerosol (5)
14 Illicit (liquor) (7)
16 Newsworthy (7)
17 Test (6)
18 Neck warmer (5)
19 Daze, trance (6)
21 Community leader (5)
22 Rough estimate (5)

Puzzle 128

ACROSS

1 Cod and potato patty (8)
6 Married women (5)
7 Rich, fertile mud or soil (4)
8 Phone button below the 9 (4)
9 Private vehicle (3)
10 Animal harness (4)
11 Engine cover (6)
13 Quake (6)
14 Take by force (6)
17 Popular fast-food item (3,3)
18 Terse (4)
20 ___ de nil, pale yellowish-green colour (3)
21 Close to (4)
22 Competent (4)
23 Sugar covering for a cake (5)
24 Grated, pared (8)

DOWN

1 Female foal (5)
2 Chain (7)
3 Loud electric horn (6)
4 Force to leave (5)
5 Flightless bird (7)
6 Snivelling (7)
12 Entering in a ledger (7)
13 Line up your sights (4,3)
15 Scanned by turning over pages (7)
16 Compound used in agriculture and glass-making (6)
17 Hot and damp, as of weather (5)
19 Latest fashion (5)

Puzzle 129

ACROSS

1 Liquid soap (4,4)
5 Junk email (4)
9 Striking distance (5)
10 Fastest overseas postal system (7)
11 Tribe in Rwanda (4)
12 Major Chinese city (8)
14 Main road built to avoid a town (6)
15 Gruesome (6)
18 Now in progress (5,3)
20 Do not include (4)
22 Person in education (7)
23 Hooded fur coat (5)
24 Highest rank in the British peerage (4)
25 Football penalty (4,4)

DOWN

1 Ruthless (5)
2 Incessant (3-4)
3 Intense grief (3)
4 Envelop (6)
6 Cook in hot water (5)
7 Appease (7)
8 Metal in its raw form (4,3)
13 Unlawful dictator (7)
14 Contused (7)
16 Medieval Japanese warrior class (7)
17 Type of sugar (6)
19 The worse for wear (5)
21 Beaten path or road (5)
23 Closed pastry-case (3)

Puzzle 130

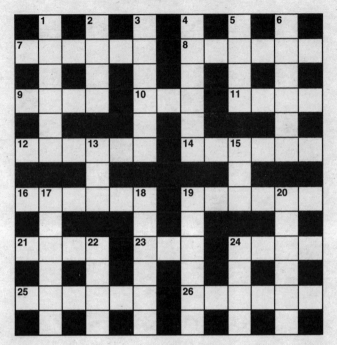

ACROSS

7 Quake with cold or fear (6)
8 Anguish (6)
9 Cygnet's parent (4)
10 Employ (3)
11 Orange's inner skin (4)
12 Public oration (6)
14 Flashily or noisily (6)
16 In a complacent manner (6)
19 Petrol-carrying vehicle (6)
21 Rounded lump or ball (4)
23 Under the alternative name of (inits) (3)
24 Put under sedation (4)
25 Genuine, real (6)
26 Sell on overseas markets (6)

DOWN

1 Put in an appearance (4,2)
2 Cooker (4)
3 Complain (6)
4 In addition (2,4)
5 Pleasure excursion (4)
6 Entrance gate (6)
13 Item consisting of albumen and yolk (3)
15 Funeral vase (3)
17 Potentially harmful person or thing (6)
18 On an annual basis (6)
19 Matching collection of crockery (3,3)
20 Sell-by date (6)
22 Wrestling match (4)
24 Hoodwink (4)

Puzzle 131

ACROSS

7 Clear (a blockage) (6)
8 Erase, obliterate (3,3)
10 Ring-tailed primate (5)
11 Farm implement (6)
13 Skin-cleansing treatment (4,4)
15 Low-pitched brass instrument (4)
17 Straightforward (4)
18 Artist's pigment jar (5,3)
21 Overflow (6)
22 Arrive eventually (3,2)
25 Royal jewelled items (6)
26 Circus marquee (3,3)

DOWN

1 Passed all relevant exams (9)
2 Dishonest plan (4)
3 Crooked, depraved (7)
4 Person who reaches a verdict (5)
5 Leaping event in athletics (4,4)
6 Money dispenser (inits) (3)
9 Long historical film (4)
12 Conduit for dirty water (5,4)
14 Accounts ledger (4,4)
16 Get by bequest (7)
19 Attaché (4)
20 Bright and warm (weather) (5)
23 Excise (4)
24 Chilly (3)

Puzzle 132

ACROSS

1 Tart-tasting (6)
8 Be reticent (4,4)
9 Firmly against (4)
10 Mesh cooking utensil (5)
11 Large weighty book (4)
12 Be representative of (6)
14 Separate from the sediment (6)
16 Lacking, non-existent (6)
19 Wild animal that lives in a sett (6)
21 Be resentful of (4)
23 Canal boat (5)
25 Den (4)
26 Ill-defined situation (4,4)
27 Enquiring impertinently (6)

DOWN

2 Transport (6)
3 Speaker's platform (4)
4 Jovial and jaunty (6)
5 Signify (6)
6 Aid in crime (4)
7 Shrewdness (6)
13 Solid water (3)
15 Ruminant's chewed food (3)
17 Numeral system that uses 0 and 1 (6)
18 Knight's tunic (6)
19 Pub worker (6)
20 Naval standard (6)
22 Toy that moves up and down on a string (2-2)
24 Nine ___, London district (4)

Puzzle 133

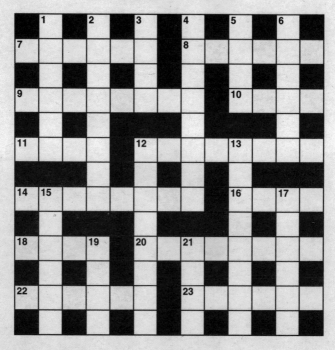

ACROSS

7 Style of architecture (6)
8 Of a book, still in pristine condition (6)
9 Talking loudly (8)
10 Must have (4)
11 Threesome (4)
12 TV talk programme (4,4)
14 Boat that carries vehicles (3,5)
16 Small upland lake (4)
18 Buddy (4)
20 Principal component (8)
22 Health centre or private hospital (6)
23 Cluster of cells that forms a small swelling (6)

DOWN

1 Female parent (6)
2 Dismiss casually (5,3)
3 ___ berry, tropical palm fruit (4)
4 Breaking and entering (8)
5 Wartime woman sailor (4)
6 Get into the habit of (4,2)
12 Pottery (8)
13 Reserve, lay by (3,5)
15 For some time (6)
17 In actual fact (6)
19 Resident of an abbey (4)
21 ___ of Court, buildings used by lawyers (4)

Puzzle 134

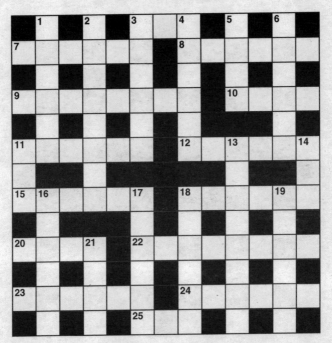

ACROSS

3 Sound of a balloon bursting (3)
7 Experienced by two or more people (6)
8 Cause, bring about (6)
9 Naturally occurring crystalline sodium chloride (4,4)
10 Trim (4)
11 Having a good knowledge of (2,4)
12 Lookalike (6)
15 Disgust (6)
18 Soft rich fabric (6)
20 Far from brand-new (4)
22 Piece of paper money (8)
23 Decorated with pictures of blooms (6)
24 Bunch of threads tied together at one end (6)
25 Never mind which (3)

DOWN

1 Popular number puzzle (6)
2 Walker's bag (8)
3 Easily influenced by others (6)
4 Marked with small dents (6)
5 Japanese noodle served in soup (4)
6 Untidy writing (6)
11 Grey long-eared animal of the horse family (3)
13 Very unattractive look (8)
14 Dine (3)
16 Treat with contempt (6)
17 Visible cloud in outer space (6)
18 Narcissism (6)
19 Regard, respect (6)
21 Shadowy (4)

Puzzle 135

ACROSS

1 Human beings (6)
4 Hold tight (6)
9 Waverers (9)
10 Washington's country (inits) (3)
11 Large tea dispenser (3)
12 Sudden epidemics (9)
13 Of water, salty (5)
15 Steer clear of (5)
20 Became rich (4,5)
22 Long-handled tool used for weeding (3)
23 Runner for sliding on snow (3)
24 Turf fans (4-5)
25 Military identification disc (3,3)
26 Housing area (6)

DOWN

1 Conductor's stand (6)
2 Many times (5)
3 Short nap on a bed (3-4)
5 Intense beam of light (5)
6 Frightening tidal wave (7)
7 Gruff, throaty (6)
8 Fixed bunk on a ship (5)
14 Getting shot (of) (7)
16 Ocean crossings (7)
17 Entertained (6)
18 Deferred indefinitely (2,3)
19 Tenant (6)
21 Black ___, police van's nickname (5)
22 'Laughing' scavenger animal (5)

Puzzle 136

ACROSS

1 Heated glass building (8)
6 Just over four weeks (5)
7 Attractive sight from a window (4)
8 Old-fashioned 'you' (4)
9 Clumsy fool (3)
10 Red gemstone (4)
11 Decayed and nasty (6)
13 Sports therapist or masseur (6)
14 Native of England, Wales or Scotland (6)
17 Recruit (staff) (4,2)
18 Milk-white precious stone (4)
20 Pair, twosome (3)
21 French for 'black' (4)
22 Very small blood-sucking insect (4)
23 Throw, hurl (5)
24 Force of personality (8)

DOWN

1 Float on a cushion of air (5)
2 Shaky, tottery (7)
3 Place to learn (6)
4 Tear-making vegetable (5)
5 Floaty see-through fabric (7)
6 Speaks indistinctly (7)
12 Closing one eye and opening it again (7)
13 Settled (a debt) (4,3)
15 Takes a drink (7)
16 Bring to a shine (6)
17 Theme to talk or write about (5)
19 South American beast of burden (5)

Puzzle 137

ACROSS

7 Indian spiced pastry (6)
8 Get together in twos (4,2)
9 Bark of a small dog (3)
10 Internet access utilising hotspots (2-2)
11 Allay (4)
13 Fawning flatterer (7)
16 Termination (3)
18 Illegal enterprise organiser (9)
21 Old name for a newt (3)
22 Composed of segments (7)
26 Office chit (4)
28 Acorn-bearing plants (4)
29 Solidify, coalesce (3)
30 Lorry fuel (6)
31 Finally, in conclusion (6)

DOWN

1 Lacking animation or interest (5)
2 Poisonous, noxious (5)
3 Retaliation (7)
4 Horrify (5)
5 Windscreen's cleaner (5)
6 Young shoots (4)
12 Swirl of water (4)
14 Hole in a needle (3)
15 Painting, drawing etc (3)
16 Go wrong (3)
17 Bug (4)
19 Noise made by a dove (3)
20 Completely (7)
22 Medieval tilting contest (5)
23 Fireside area (5)
24 Put out (a candle) (5)
25 Bony framework of the head (5)
27 Wicked, bad (4)

Puzzle 138

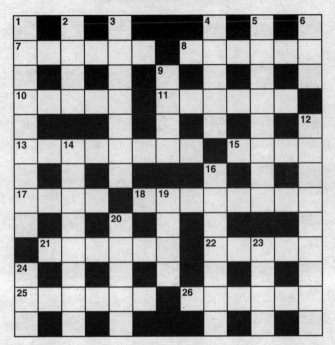

ACROSS

7 Setting (a table) (6)
8 Being borrowed (from the library) (2,4)
10 Hot pursuit (5)
11 Elegant, up-market (6)
13 Admiring greatly (8)
15 Greek cheese (4)
17 War between families (4)
18 Serving time? (2,6)
21 Laundry slides (6)
22 Family saying (5)
25 Cement mix (6)
26 Preacher's platform (6)

DOWN

1 Pass a current through (9)
2 Vega's constellation (4)
3 Not listened to (7)
4 Tell tales (5)
5 Beer mats (8)
6 Common joining word (3)
9 Of poetry, be metrically correct (4)
12 Waterproof outdoor garments (9)
14 Slips offering a discount (8)
16 Knowingly false charge (5-2)
19 Organ for smelling (4)
20 Narrow band of leather (5)
23 Lightweight sun hat (4)
24 Mischievous elf (3)

Puzzle 139

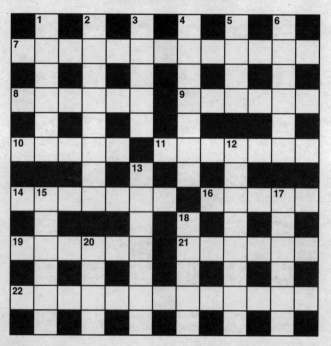

ACROSS

7 Opponent of state interference (13)
8 Abundant wealth (6)
9 Strong shoe (6)
10 Book of maps (5)
11 Tell me if you've got enough! (3,4)
14 Swaying to and fro (7)
16 Vigorous, quick (5)
19 Division of a long poem (6)
21 Indubitably (6)
22 Well-deserved punishment or reward (6,7)

DOWN

1 Smear with oil (6)
2 Glass container for water creatures (4-4)
3 Before all others (5)
4 Bête noire (7)
5 In addition (4)
6 Take as read (6)
12 Productivity (4,4)
13 Early stages (7)
15 Choice (6)
17 Emotional comfort (6)
18 Debatable point (5)
20 Hard-shelled fruits (4)

Puzzle 140

ACROSS

- **1** Saw, maxim (5)
- **4** Snide grin (5)
- **10** Layered board (7)
- **11** Brazilian music (5)
- **12** Skin irritation (4)
- **13** Table coaster? (5,3)
- **16** Victory cup or plate (6)
- **17** Be in agreement (6)
- **20** Diplomacy (8)
- **21** Overly moral person (4)
- **23** Soil fertiliser (5)
- **25** Variety of leather (7)
- **26** Roman numeral XL (5)
- **27** Facial-hair growth (5)

DOWN

- **2** College for non-boarders (3,6)
- **3** Well-behaved (4)
- **5** Tuneful container! (5,3)
- **6** Edge of a glass (3)
- **7** Race at full speed (6)
- **8** Pastoral scene (5)
- **9** Dray (4)
- **14** Scandalmonger (9)
- **15** Gossip (8)
- **18** Furiously angry (6)
- **19** Range (5)
- **20** Dancing-shoe (4)
- **22** Leer (4)
- **24** Old card game (3)

Puzzle 141

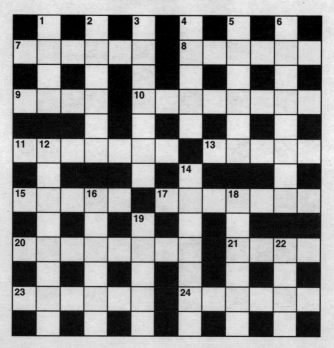

ACROSS

7 Arrive (4,2)
8 Inaccurate (6)
9 Awry (4)
10 Property rentals (8)
11 Warehouse (space) (7)
13 Ponderous (5)
15 Misty (5)
17 Table silverware (7)
20 Conflict within a nation (5,3)
21 Unit of electric potential (4)
23 Kitchen weighing machine (6)
24 Going wrong (6)

DOWN

1 Zero in cricket (4)
2 Response (to a question) (6)
3 Regretful acknowledgement of an error or failing (7)
4 Is painful (5)
5 Line of colour (6)
6 Suffering the after-effects of alcohol (4-4)
12 Garment consisting of matching items (3-5)
14 Group of four (7)
16 Fiercely, sternly (6)
18 Romantic partners (6)
19 Move through the air, making a rushing sound (5)
22 Touch down (4)

Puzzle 142

ACROSS

1 Scene from above (5-3,4)
9 Fine quality coffee bean (5)
10 Japanese art of folding paper (7)
11 Unharmonious (8)
12 Religious subgroup (4)
14 Lubricate (6)
15 Imp-like person (6)
18 Flick of a coin (4)
20 Designated by an inappropriate name (2-6)
23 Token (7)
24 Association of tradesmen (5)
25 In a comforting manner (12)

DOWN

2 Make very angry (7)
3 A completely useless person (4,4)
4 Self-importance (6)
5 Long adventure story (4)
6 Fuming (5)
7 Essential item for a referee (7)
8 Give off (4)
13 Aerosol paint dispenser (5,3)
14 Put across (3,4)
16 Hostility (3-4)
17 Revulsion (6)
19 Finnish steam bath (5)
21 Old-fashioned decorative skirting (4)
22 Initials on British government correspondence (inits) (4)

Puzzle 143

ACROSS

1 Simply too much! (12)
9 Accommodation (at a meal) (7)
10 Quash (5)
11 Border upon (4)
12 Branch of mathematics (7)
15 Fruits such as lemons and limes (6)
16 Dynamic, powerful (6)
19 School's senior male prefect (4,3)
21 Added to (4)
24 White gems (5)
25 Ship's captain (7)
26 State of eagerly awaiting (12)

DOWN

2 Road bridge (7)
3 Attack (4)
4 Immensely (6)
5 Exclude, omit (5,3)
6 Part of a target next to the bull's-eye (5)
7 Metal found in nuggets (4)
8 Disapprovingly, with disdain (7)
13 Street or passage closed at one end (3-2-3)
14 Offensive sight (7)
17 West Indian ballad (7)
18 Idle chatter (6)
20 Specific (5)
22 Lounge furniture item (4)
23 Shrivel, become limp (4)

Puzzle 144

ACROSS

1 Scrumptious (5)
4 Homage (7)
9 Empty, vacant (8)
10 Natural colour of linen (4)
11 Dog-faced monkey (6)
12 Engage (6)
13 Impossible to transfer to someone else (3-10)
17 Cut into strips (6)
19 Say aloud to an audience (6)
21 Study intensively (4)
22 I beg your pardon (6,2)
23 Urge (7)
24 Bedeck (5)

DOWN

2 Amphitheatre (5)
3 Restrict (3,4)
5 Beef or lamb, eg (3,4)
6 Sound of a radio signal (5)
7 Commotion (7)
8 Amaze (4)
14 Metal cylinder containing fuel (3,4)
15 Atheistic (7)
16 Prisoner in a court of law (7)
18 Welsh name for Wales (5)
19 Heap of hay, straw etc (4)
20 Clock-like device used when cooking (5)

Puzzle 145

ACROSS

1 Strict hermit (7)
4 Russian ruler (4)
9 Variety of gym exercise (5-2)
11 Fully grown (5)
12 Triangular river-mouth (5)
13 Exact (4,2)
15 Disarrange (6)
17 Thrash about in pain (6)
19 Frustrate, thwart (6)
20 Biblical tower (5)
23 Ancient cereal grain (5)
24 Hinder completely (7)
25 Give medicine to (4)
26 Make arrangements (for) (7)

DOWN

2 Move silently (5)
3 Force upon (6)
5 Prolonged (4-3)
6 Grooves made by wheels (4)
7 Eight-legged websters (7)
8 Auspicious (10)
10 Horse inhabiting the same place as another (10)
14 Fervent devotees (7)
16 Health (7)
18 Very angry state (6)
21 Amalgam (5)
22 Far from brand-new (4)

Puzzle 146

ACROSS

1 Consuming desire (7)
5 Place your foot (4)
10 Contrary in position (7)
11 Broadcasting live (2,3)
12 Bundle of unthreshed corn (5)
13 Lightness (6)
15 Sound of something being hit (6)
17 Offspring of two different species (6)
19 Ornamental cave (6)
20 Speeds (5)
23 House of ice (5)
24 Aristocracy (7)
25 Be the breadwinner (4)
26 Art of public speaking (7)

DOWN

2 Topical entertainment (5)
3 Proof (12)
4 Pine spike (6)
6 Device for grilling bread (7)
7 Flesh of a pig used as meat (4)
8 Bearded (7)
9 Factory's moving production line (8,4)
14 Greek epic poem (7)
16 Songbird such as the whitethroat (7)
18 Press stud (6)
21 Seat for one (5)
22 Thin fencing material (4)

Puzzle 147

ACROSS

1 Cheapen, lower the value of (6)
4 Achieve (6)
9 Chewy confections (7)
10 Indicate similarities between (5)
11 Move quickly here and there (4)
12 Ophthalmological examination (3,4)
14 Swear in as a minister (6)
16 Extremely busy (6)
19 In an aircraft or ship (2,5)
21 Apple seeds (4)
23 Jewish leader or teacher (5)
24 Tuition periods (7)
25 Formal and elaborate (of clothes) (6)
26 Large birds of prey (6)

DOWN

1 Time (of an event) (4)
2 Bewildered (7)
3 Parted with money (5)
5 Feel sure of the truth of (7)
6 Joint between the foot and leg (5)
7 Easy-cleaning (pots and pans) (3-5)
8 Crooked, awry (5)
13 Given a prestigious award (8)
15 Sloping script (7)
17 Upper layer of earth in the garden (7)
18 Strangely (5)
20 Old and New Testaments (5)
21 Spaghetti or lasagne, for example (5)
22 Employs (4)

Puzzle 148

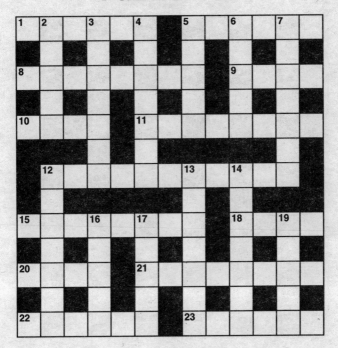

ACROSS

1 Finished or shut (6)
5 Single long step (6)
8 Method of surface mining (4-4)
9 Deep affection (4)
10 List of available dishes (4)
11 Mass slaughter (8)
12 Bearing marks of frequent handling (4,7)
15 Behaving stealthily (8)
18 Average (4)
20 Grows older (4)
21 Ex-sweetheart (3,5)
22 Farrier's workshop (6)
23 Toady, sycophant (3-3)

DOWN

2 Temporary slip (5)
3 Gratifying to the body (7)
4 Current of air flowing through a room (7)
5 Demonstration where protesters refuse to budge (3-2)
6 Object of historic interest (5)
7 Apportioned, split up (7)
12 Chewy fruit-flavoured sweet (4,3)
13 Profane (7)
14 Arm or leg bracelets (7)
16 Something worth having (5)
17 Tusk substance (5)
19 Energetic Cuban dance (5)

Puzzle 149

ACROSS

7 Child rendered parentless (6)
8 Replete, sated (4,2)
10 Torvill or Dean? (3-6)
11 Which people? (3)
12 Short-term insurance certificate (5,4)
14 Near or towards the stern of a boat (3)
15 Mate (3)
16 Toy used for jumping (4,5)
18 End of a pen (3)
20 Warning of a conflagration (4,5)
21 Dine away from home (3,3)
22 Pass (time) (4,2)

DOWN

1 Astrological signs (6)
2 Thorough change or movement (8)
3 Painted curtain to the rear of the stage (8)
4 Noise made by a contented cat (4)
5 Fault (4)
6 Germinate (6)
9 Violent (6-3)
13 Blissful (8)
14 In a friendly fashion (8)
15 Gratify, give satisfaction (6)
17 Japanese dress (6)
19 Water barrel (4)
20 Offensive (4)

Puzzle 150

ACROSS

1 Devastate (6)
4 Scale (a ladder) (5)
8 Available for renting (2,3)
9 Faded celebrity (3-4)
10 Tanned hide (7)
11 Antlered animal (4)
12 Butt, cask (3)
14 Greek cheese (4)
15 Drubbing (4)
18 Gene code (inits) (3)
21 Makeshift boat (4)
23 Club (7)
25 Soldier's dugout (7)
26 Inception (5)
27 The present time (5)
28 Sanctuary (6)

DOWN

1 Baby's toy (6)
2 Small settlement (7)
3 Advance (3,5)
4 Snug (4)
5 Incompetent (5)
6 Genial (6)
7 Predatory fish (5)
13 Affable (8)
16 Kitchen tool (7)
17 Business return (6)
19 Residue of a fire (5)
20 Process (6)
22 Repaired (5)
24 Lean, gaunt (4)

Puzzle 151

ACROSS

7 Predict (8)
8 Middle leg joint (4)
10 Museum official (7)
11 Furry, covered in down (5)
12 Reveal (4)
13 Injecting device (7)
16 Meal for which a wok is useful (4-3)
18 In a position (to) (4)
22 Sorcerer's power (5)
24 Theatrical sense of style (7)
25 Elevator (4)
26 Suddenly divulge (5,3)

DOWN

1 Aromatic flavourings added to food (6)
2 Part of the framework of an entrance (8)
3 Sliding trough (5)
4 Towards evil ways (6)
5 Against (4)
6 Blue-green gemstone (5)
9 Belonging to more than one person (5)
14 Retract (a promise) (2,4,2)
15 Clever prank (5)
17 Undulate (6)
19 Occurrences, happenings (6)
20 Happy or friendly facial expression (5)
21 Catch in a trap (5)
23 Natural talent (4)

Puzzle 152

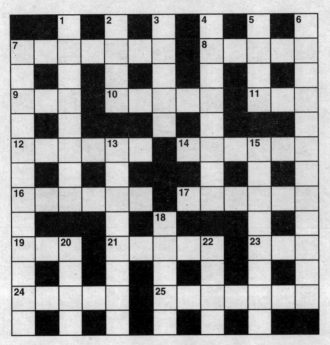

ACROSS

7 Plant that grows up a wall (7)
8 Main table in a church (5)
9 Handled beaker (3)
10 Bald ___, US symbol (5)
11 Mischievous fairy (3)
12 Open by means of a key (6)
14 ___ poker, spiky plant (3-3)
16 Add to, improve (6)
17 Blood product (6)
19 Bitterly cold (3)
21 Yellowish-beige in colour (5)
23 Animal in a farrow (3)
24 Full of desire and enthusiasm (5)
25 Most important worker (7)

DOWN

1 One-off (8)
2 Slender woodwind instrument (4)
3 Impurities which fall to the bottom of a drink (5)
4 Goodbye (8)
5 Affliction of the eyelid (4)
6 Indicator of a business's success (6,6)
7 Of information, converted to digital data (12)
13 Too confident (8)
15 Garden-watering tube (8)
18 Scaly carnivorous reptile (5)
20 Meditative discipline (4)
22 Tug violently (4)

Puzzle 153

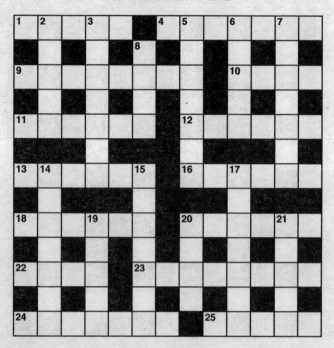

ACROSS

1 Smears, splatters (5)
4 Since, as (7)
9 Expired (8)
10 Objects to play with (4)
11 Add, append (6)
12 Standing by (2,4)
13 Supported on water (6)
16 Receipt of admission (6)
18 Treasurer (6)
20 Showy (6)
22 False god (4)
23 Develop and hatch (eggs) (8)
24 Word meaning the same as another (7)
25 Chart (5)

DOWN

2 Ward off (5)
3 Swaggering show of boldness (7)
5 Ultimate (7)
6 Upper storey (5)
7 Azure (3-4)
8 Firmly mark (4)
14 Ironworks (7)
15 Frighten (7)
17 Large room for official functions (7)
19 Simultaneous firing of weapons, often in salute (5)
20 Truth (4)
21 Increase in temperature (3,2)

Puzzle 154

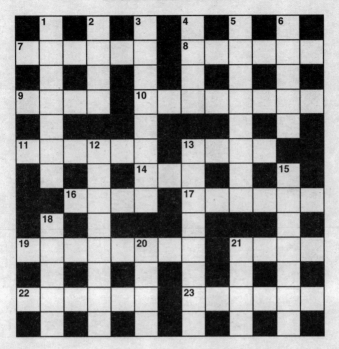

ACROSS

7 Present for consideration (6)
8 Ridges in fingerprints (6)
9 Antlered male deer (4)
10 Wanted by lots of people (2,6)
11 Strong drink (6)
13 Short ballet skirt (4)
14 Otherwise closest bid (inits) (3)
16 Centre of a pencil (4)
17 Least young (6)
19 Round trip of inns (3,5)
21 Spiral (4)
22 Rose to a great height (6)
23 Robber who flies the Jolly Roger (6)

DOWN

1 Window cover (7)
2 Polluted mist (4)
3 Bar used to secure a carpet (5,3)
4 Due to be repaid (4)
5 Travelled to and from work (8)
6 Abrupt, plain-spoken (5)
12 Second-hand vehicles (4,4)
13 Cyclists' foot supports (3-5)
15 Short-sleeved tops (1-6)
18 English royal house (5)
20 Military assistant (4)
21 Feel concern (4)

Puzzle 155

ACROSS

6 Pond's water-spouting ornament (8)
8 Juice of freshly picked grapes (4)
10 Emit, give off (5)
11 Mark, blot (6)
13 Fee for using a bridge (4)
14 Delusional feeling of threat (8)
16 Via terra firma (8)
19 Sign of an old wound (4)
22 Crustacean similar to a prawn (6)
23 Wild, frenetic (5)
25 Jobbing journalist (4)
26 Small fatty fish, often canned (8)

DOWN

1 Loving warmth (9)
2 Trusty horse (5)
3 Midday nap (6)
4 Eager, zealous (4-2)
5 Money dispenser (inits) (3)
7 Commonplace (5)
9 Wall picture (5)
12 Improvised street obstacle (9)
15 Shifting, unpredictable (5)
17 Science of morals (6)
18 Serviette (6)
20 Dance involving a line of people (5)
21 Strike with an open hand (5)
24 Question word answered by 'because' (3)

Puzzle 156

ACROSS

1 Radiator and boiler system (7)
5 Black playing-card (5)
9 Arduous journey (4)
10 Round metal bottle top (5,3)
11 Stage in development (5)
12 Praise publicly (7)
14 Secondary route (6)
16 Of inferior quality (6)
18 Studious (7)
20 Convulsion (5)
22 Gin-based cocktail (4,4)
24 Golf club (4)
25 Friendship (5)
26 Assert again (7)

DOWN

2 Relating to life on this planet (7)
3 Assess, review (4,5)
4 Deep Scottish loch (4)
6 Foot of an animal (3)
7 Sewer (5)
8 Missiles shot from a bow (6)
13 Issue open to debate (4,5)
15 Depressing (6)
17 Mete (4,3)
19 Drug extracted from a type of poppy (5)
21 Rubber wheel-surround (4)
23 Self-assembly set (3)

Puzzle 157

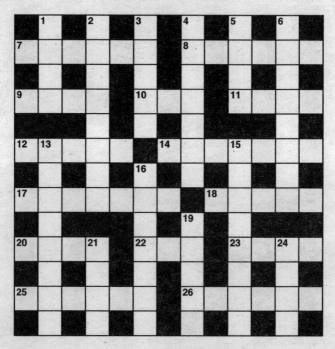

ACROSS

7 Disco light (6)
8 Cheap and gaudy (6)
9 Produced young (4)
10 ___ de cologne, light perfume (3)
11 Encounter (4)
12 On top (5)
14 Economically sound (7)
17 Quickly, sharply (7)
18 Unexpected plot change (5)
20 Pre-owned, second-hand (4)
22 Large rounded vase (3)
23 Solemn promise (4)
25 Pertaining to nuclear energy (6)
26 Sleazy and unsavoury (6)

DOWN

1 Object in the sky (4)
2 Postpone (4,4)
3 Round flat hat (5)
4 Pastry roll filled with fruit (7)
5 Take a dip (4)
6 Early trousers (8)
13 Area flattened by air-raids (4,4)
15 Trial venue (3,5)
16 Having frilly layers (7)
19 Pent-up worry (5)
21 Large cupola (4)
24 Work very hard (4)

Puzzle 158

ACROSS

1 Stained, shaded (with) (6)
5 Yield to low spirits (4)
8 Course for horses (9)
9 Section of a curve (3)
11 Female horse (4)
12 Time that a planned operation starts (4,4)
14 Conference, discussion (6)
16 Shed against a wall (4-2)
18 From the Far East (8)
19 Metallic element used in galvanising (4)
22 Consume (3)
23 Unpleasant jobs passed on to another (5,4)
24 Spring up (4)
25 Stop, cease (6)

DOWN

2 Bring upon yourself (5)
3 Becomes (4)
4 Sliding box in a cabinet (6)
5 Thorough remodelling (8)
6 Body of soldiers (7)
7 Old record player (10)
10 Sweet baked treat made with root vegetable (6,4)
13 Enlisted (6,2)
15 Pare (7)
17 Strong aversion (6)
20 Chains, fetters (5)
21 Seeing organs (4)

Puzzle 159

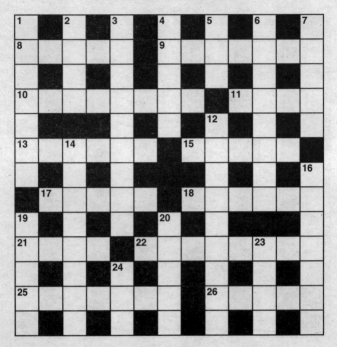

ACROSS

8 Middle Eastern sweet of crushed sesame seeds (5)
9 Was of great height (7)
10 Stalking (8)
11 Pole used as a ship's mast (4)
13 Shrewd, sharp-witted (6)
15 Bend (5)
17 Splendid, magnificent (5)
18 Follow a course like a helix (6)
21 Travel as a passenger (4)
22 Storage space for books, eg (8)
25 Concave overhead (7)
26 Speech medium (5)

DOWN

1 French manor house (7)
2 Emotional request (4)
3 Art of selling (9)
4 Bad odour (5)
5 Number in a duet (3)
6 Lose your footing (4,4)
7 Revere deeply (5)
12 Teenage crush? (5,4)
14 Whacked (5,3)
16 Paved (7)
19 Show to be true (5)
20 Degree of colour (5)
23 Greek goddess of the rainbow (4)
24 And so forth (abbrev.) (3)

Puzzle 160

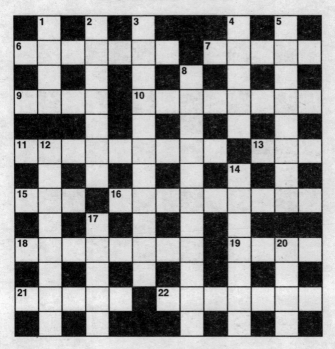

ACROSS

6 Quickened (7)
7 Regular pounding (5)
9 Fruit peel (4)
10 Good-natured (8)
11 Riches (9)
13 Electric-cable coating (inits) (3)
15 Touchdown in rugby (3)
16 Art of cultivating and selling blooms (9)
18 Green or purple vegetable (8)
19 Coaching houses (4)
21 Expend (3,2)
22 Without frills (7)

DOWN

1 Animal secretion used in perfumes (4)
2 To be honest (7)
3 Begin to appreciate (3,1,4,3)
4 Low-cost (5)
5 Astonish (4,4)
8 Noticeable (11)
12 Potential blaze? (4,4)
14 Common painkiller (7)
17 Talent seeker (5)
20 Void (4)

Puzzle 161

ACROSS

1 Tale with a message (8)
5 Flat round plate (4)
8 Machine for cassettes (4,4)
9 Jumping parasite (4)
11 Nibble persistently (4)
12 Model of excellence (7)
14 Torpor, indifference (6)
16 Religious verses (6)
18 Wrap around (7)
19 All singularly (4)
22 Summer solstice's month (4)
23 Overhead train running on one track (8)
24 Colour of most squirrels (4)
25 Travellers (8)

DOWN

1 Ostentatiously creative (4)
2 Garden plant with flowers on long spikes (5)
3 Decline (2,8)
4 Set of cooking instructions (6)
6 Criminal (7)
7 Insular, tribal (8)
10 Fed up (7,3)
13 Washstand pitcher (5,3)
15 Put forward, suggest (7)
17 Commotion (6)
20 Rub painfully (5)
21 As well as (4)

Puzzle 162

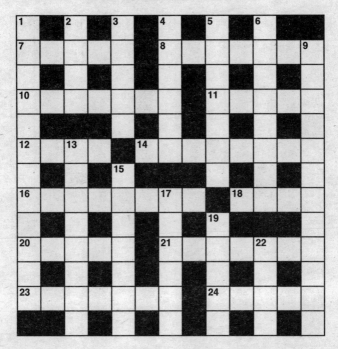

ACROSS

7 Place of access (5)
8 Give in (to) (7)
10 Naturally grown (7)
11 Large stringed instrument (5)
12 Related by blood (4)
14 Extremely dark colour (3,5)
16 Gatecrasher (8)
18 Man of courage (4)
20 Standard of perfection (5)
21 Cosmetic goo applied thickly to the face (3,4)
23 Sparkle (7)
24 Confederation (5)

DOWN

1 Dispiriting (12)
2 ___ party, pre-wedding occasion (4)
3 Reclining (5)
4 Human mental or spiritual faculty (6)
5 Block of frozen water (3,4)
6 Head-on (portrait) (4-4)
9 Making a group reservation (5-7)
13 Fearless, unafraid (8)
15 Degree or level of excellence (7)
17 Stoat's fur (6)
19 Find the total of (3,2)
22 Centre of rotation (4)

Puzzle 163

ACROSS

7 Energetic political campaigning (12)
9 Senseless talk (7)
10 Scent (5)
11 Seaside projection (4)
12 Sudden involuntary kick (4-4)
14 Ingests, gulps down (8)
17 Mellowed (4)
20 Small with a delicate frame (5)
21 Slight, insubstantial (7)
23 Dressmaking aid (7,5)

DOWN

1 Join on to (4)
2 Secret, mysterious (6)
3 Actor's comment directed at the audience (5)
4 Appoint by ballot (4,2)
5 Speared (7)
6 Witticism aimed at just a few (2-4)
8 Indicated (6)
11 Delicate hue (6)
13 Unseeingly (7)
15 Street disturbance (6)
16 Diluted (6)
18 Dreary (6)
19 Disparaging (5)
22 Expresses in words (4)

Puzzle 164

ACROSS

1 Stop from exploding (6)
4 Bird with a huge beak (6)
9 Before (5,2)
10 Protect (5)
11 Welsh breed of dog (5)
12 Louts (7)
13 Purpose (5)
15 Rising sharply (5)
20 Pilot (7)
22 Subsequently (5)
24 Social blunder (5)
25 Pressed into folds, like a kilt (7)
26 Programme in advance (6)
27 Rise (6)

DOWN

1 Show, portray (6)
2 Mendicant monk (5)
3 Wave riding (7)
5 Mouth ___, harmonica (5)
6 Absurd pretence (7)
7 Naked sun-worshipper (6)
8 Crack (puzzles) (5)
14 Runny nose (7)
16 Tours (7)
17 Attach to a hook (4,2)
18 Swathe (5)
19 Praise (6)
21 At that place (5)
23 Designation (5)

Puzzle 165

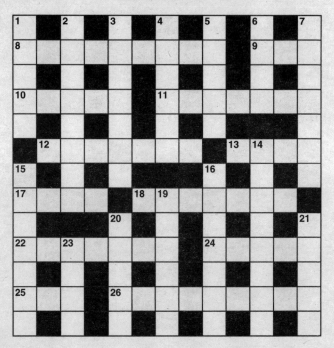

ACROSS

8 Ignite (3,6)
9 Furnish with weapons (3)
10 Royal domain (5)
11 Openwork fabric (7)
12 Via (7)
13 Open-topped pie (4)
17 Bookie's prices (4)
18 Imposing structure (7)
22 Fruity spicy preserve (7)
24 One who purchases (5)
25 Criticise continually (3)
26 Breach (9)

DOWN

1 Assume (authority) by force (5)
2 Fastened (8)
3 Stump (7)
4 Drink of yolk, beer and spirit (3-3)
5 Condition (5)
6 Traditional Hindu dress (4)
7 Picture to yourself (7)
14 Bran tub or prize draw (5,3)
15 Pig-like (7)
16 Eccentric (7)
19 Timber fungus (3,3)
20 Scoundrel (5)
21 Main part of a tree (5)
23 Compulsion (4)

Puzzle 166

ACROSS

1 Glass box for exhibiting items (7,4)
8 Container with a handle and a spout (6)
9 Uncomfortably hot and humid (6)
10 Hold, restrain (4)
11 Saint or prophet, eg (3,2,3)
13 Verdant (5)
15 Take possession of (territory) (5)
18 Highly regarded (8)
19 Pour down (4)
20 Cereal, fruit and nut breakfast dish (6)
21 Firm, unfaltering (6)
22 Cleansing agent (7,4)

DOWN

2 Immobile state (9)
3 Wild red flower (5)
4 Conker-playing time of year (6)
5 Gaming establishment (6)
6 Harden (7)
7 Looked at (4)
12 Far from closely defined (4-5)
14 Flower of the iris family (7)
16 Teasingly mischievous (6)
17 More than probable (4-2)
18 Television industry award (4)
19 The pre-20 years (5)

Puzzle 167

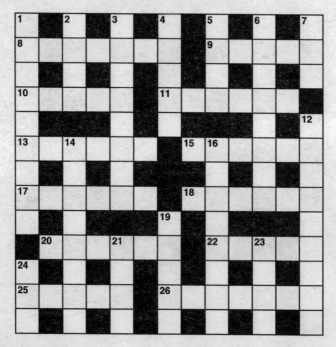

ACROSS

8 Certainly (2,5)
9 Undisguised (5)
10 To do with the kidneys (5)
11 Certifier of deeds (6)
13 Axle-end cover (3-3)
15 Out of the country (6)
17 Ghostly, creepy (6)
18 Betrothed man (6)
20 Practical (6)
22 Picture playing-cards (5)
25 Full of fumes (5)
26 Panacea (4-3)

DOWN

1 Complete absence of law or government (9)
2 Biblical paradise (4)
3 Use seniority to obtain privileges (4,4)
4 Gravelled (5)
5 Crossbow arrow (4)
6 Tire by relentless pressure (4,4)
7 Had a meal (3)
12 In a harmful way (9)
14 Paperback store (8)
16 Eye-pieces worn by horses (8)
19 Clemency (5)
21 Young lads (4)
23 Opposite of 'far' (4)
24 Supernatural power (inits) (3)

Puzzle 168

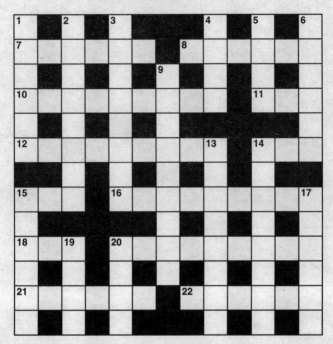

ACROSS

7 Complete, whole-hearted (3-3)
8 Handled container (6)
10 In an optimistic manner (9)
11 Church bench (3)
12 Present in a new way (9)
14 Green shell containing peas (3)
15 Isolated mass of rock (3)
16 Condition of being filthy (9)
18 Musical pitch (3)
20 Far-sighted (9)
21 Selfish and nasty (6)
22 Pasture plant (6)

DOWN

1 Thin slice of bacon (6)
2 Insect trap (8)
3 Appeared from underwater (8)
4 Violent rage (4)
5 Large waste container (4)
6 Cooked slowly in liquid (6)
9 Area for storing hats and coats (9)
13 Worthy to be chosen (8)
14 Keep from decay (8)
15 Shorten (a garment) (4,2)
17 Medical stitch (6)
19 Harness together (4)
20 Colour of coral or salmon (4)

Puzzle 169

ACROSS

1 Crisp biscuit for ice cream (5)
4 White mineral found in bones and teeth (7)
8 Child supervision facilities (3,4)
9 Sound of pain (5)
10 Midday (4)
11 Thirsty (3)
12 Old folk tale or legend (4)
15 Infectious (of a tune) (6)
16 Piercing, ear-splitting (6)
19 Nocturnal birds (4)
21 Computer software facility (abbrev.) (3)
22 Bird similar to a rook (4)
26 Diary insertion (5)
27 Mimic (7)
28 Warm in advance (7)
29 Passenger vehicles (5)

DOWN

1 Make broader (5)
2 Advertise in unauthorised places (3-4)
3 Look at books (4)
4 Gladdens (6)
5 Part of a company's image (4)
6 Mockery of fate (5)
7 Flavouring with a cool taste (7)
13 Afraid of attention (3)
14 For what purpose? (3)
15 Near view (5-2)
17 Penetration (7)
18 Ruined (6)
20 Liquid measure (5)
23 Periods of seven days (5)
24 Ancient Greek stringed instrument (4)
25 Branch of a tree (4)

Puzzle 170

ACROSS

1 Half of a hundred (5)
4 Second line of a rugby scrum (4,3)
8 Curved inwards (7)
9 Shock greatly (5)
10 Steep decline (4)
11 Used a spade (3)
12 Against (4)
15 Lancashire dish (6)
16 Secretarial skill (6)
19 Part of the ear (4)
21 Money dispenser (inits) (3)
22 Notice, espy (4)
26 Small cove (5)
27 Existing on company premises (2-5)
28 Judicial trial (7)
29 Young soldier (5)

DOWN

1 Confronted (5)
2 Bring to light (4,3)
3 Twelve months (4)
4 Detonated (4,2)
5 Scottish tribe (4)
6 Develop (5)
7 Consenting (7)
13 In what manner? (3)
14 Room with cross-trainers and treadmills (3)
15 Horrendous, infernal (7)
17 Seize (7)
18 Twine (6)
20 Model-aeroplane wood (5)
23 Use a mobile-blogging site (5)
24 Small case for holding needles, cotton (4)
25 Stylish elegance (4)

Puzzle 171

ACROSS

1 Value-adjusted (5-6)
9 Defeated player (5)
10 Deprived of (7)
11 Envisage (7)
12 Skirt fold (5)
13 Colour of jet (5)
15 Computer-data storage medium (1,1-3)
20 Book used in collecting and mounting stamps (5)
22 Ceremonial procession (7)
24 Nightclub doorman (7)
25 Hut (5)
26 Interpret a clock's hands (4,3,4)

DOWN

2 Air passage near the septum (7)
3 Noblemen (5)
4 Modest, understated (3-3)
5 Journalist's tool of the trade (7)
6 Arouse (5)
7 Escarpment (5)
8 Nation (5)
14 Laughable (7)
16 Bowling style (7)
17 Drivers' stopping place (3-2)
18 Burn, singe (6)
19 Reaches the highest point (5)
21 Monster (5)
23 Take an exam again (5)

Puzzle 172

ACROSS

1 Reject (4,3)
5 Darts player's starting point (4)
10 Slow irregular flow of liquid (7)
11 Cook's pinny (5)
12 Party dance (5)
13 Earring for non-pierced ears (4-2)
15 Illusory, imaginary (6)
17 Employment office (6)
19 Amusing TV show (6)
20 Proportion (5)
23 Dessert or pudding (5)
24 Noisy or unrestrained merrymaking (7)
25 Morse code element (4)
26 Female who will receive the family fortune (7)

DOWN

2 Straighten (5)
3 Quite like (4,1,5,2)
4 Savage (6)
6 Animation (7)
7 Sea eagle (4)
8 ___ for, defend (5,2)
9 Formula One competitor, eg (6,6)
14 Word with the same meaning (7)
16 Plunderers (7)
18 Surface (6)
21 Rings (church bells) (5)
22 Far from brand-new (4)

Puzzle 173

ACROSS

1 Gadget, contraption (6)
4 Nestle down (on a sofa) (4,2)
9 Elegantly mannered (7)
10 Benefactor (5)
11 Style of late-1970s rock music (4)
12 Embedded (4-3)
14 Wide tree-lined street (6)
16 Place of refuge (6)
19 Period during which a cricket team is batting (7)
21 Minute opening in the surface of the skin (4)
23 Irate emotion (5)
24 Reminiscent of a corpse (7)
25 Baby cat (6)
26 Chest (6)

DOWN

1 Continually follows (4)
2 Project, exploit (7)
3 Harsh noise (of an unoiled hinge, for example) (5)
5 Remove your clothes (7)
6 Byroads (5)
7 Occupying less than a full working week (4-4)
8 Single leaf of grass (5)
13 Row of cabs (4,4)
15 Perturb (7)
17 Greyhound cross-breed (7)
18 In reserve (5)
20 Time of darkness (5)
21 Cook slowly in boiling liquid (5)
22 Large American wild cat (4)

Puzzle 174

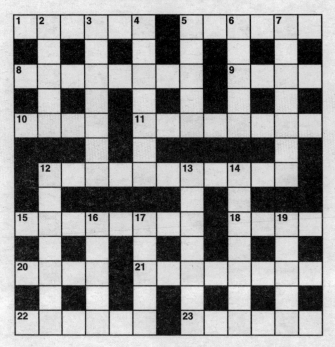

ACROSS

1 Military knapsack (3-3)
5 Limp (6)
8 Tweak (4-4)
9 South London cricket ground (4)
10 Port south of Beirut (4)
11 Following (8)
12 Police group always ready for action (6,5)
15 Spanning (8)
18 Drainage reservoir (4)
20 Dull sound of impact (4)
21 Make a hasty assessment of (8)
22 Pleasantly windy (6)
23 In an orderly way (6)

DOWN

2 Very coldly (5)
3 Fermenting plant (7)
4 Person who eats to excess (7)
5 'Laughing' beast (5)
6 Babbling stream (5)
7 Educated (7)
12 Additional (7)
13 Part of an orange, eg (7)
14 Flawed, defective (7)
16 Avoid (5)
17 Suggest (5)
19 Rich powerful person (5)

Puzzle 175

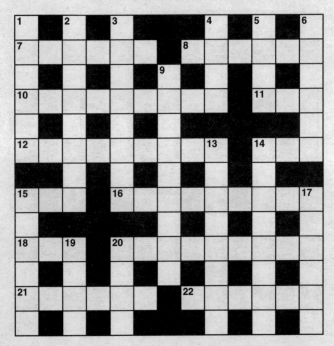

ACROSS

7 Countermand (6)
8 Mini-marathon in aid of charity (3,3)
10 UK's banner (5,4)
11 Fifth sign of the zodiac (3)
12 VIPs' dining bench (4,5)
14 Scoundrel (3)
15 Baronet's title (3)
16 Sureness, confidence (9)
18 Edge of a glass (3)
20 Nod off (2,2,5)
21 Facilitate (6)
22 Thick liquid applied to the skin (6)

DOWN

1 Squat down (6)
2 Breed of spaniel (8)
3 Possessing powers of attraction (8)
4 (Had) tolled (4)
5 Inland Asian sea (4)
6 Open (a map) (6)
9 Expand (9)
13 Release, outflow (8)
14 Fossil fuel before refining (5,3)
15 Grouped (6)
17 Use up (time or energy) (6)
19 Tight-fisted (4)
20 Swallow (drink) noisily (4)

Puzzle 176

ACROSS

1 Plume or crest of feathers (7)
5 Breeding stallion (4)
10 Anything remaining (5)
11 Fidelity (7)
12 Economic recovery (7)
14 Elephant's long tooth (4)
16 Compel forcibly (6)
18 Sell on overseas markets (6)
20 Go out of focus (4)
21 Continue (5,2)
24 Erase (4,3)
25 Defendant's whereabouts claim (5)
27 Period over Christmas (4)
28 Snakes which suffocate their prey (7)

DOWN

2 ___ for, decide on (3)
3 Brown uniform cloth (5)
4 Accommodate (6)
6 Exaggerated yarn (4,5)
7 Periods of time (4)
8 Having outlived its usefulness (7)
9 Grammatical arrangement (6)
13 Abrasive made from metal (5,4)
15 Person covering for another's non-appearance (5-2)
17 ___ off, enclose (6)
19 Forgetful, disorganised (6)
22 Arrive at (5)
23 Deftly (4)
26 Charged atomic particle (3)

Puzzle 177

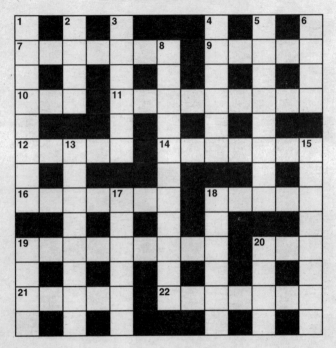

ACROSS

7 Pursuing (7)
9 Further, additional (5)
10 Uncanny foresight (inits) (3)
11 Episode of severe winter weather (9)
12 Meditates (5)
14 Dandified (7)
16 Noisily make merry (7)
18 Set principle (5)
19 Carved shape for display (9)
20 Judge's head covering (3)
21 Unsavoury broth (5)
22 Former (7)

DOWN

1 Ribbon of coloured paper (8)
2 Continually complain (4)
3 Affectionate pecks (6)
4 Even chance or choice (4-2)
5 Giving a cry of triumph (8)
6 Stern, severe (4)
8 Luck (4,7)
13 Action provoking a response (8)
15 Senior female prefect (4,4)
17 Overturn or collapse (6)
18 Dismal, dull (6)
19 Herb used in stuffing (4)
20 Mourn audibly (4)

Puzzle 178

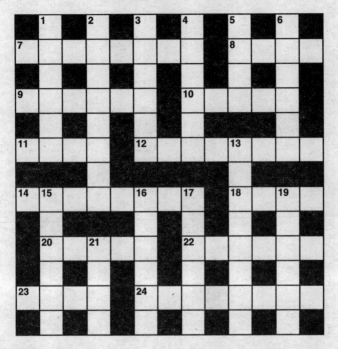

ACROSS

7 Tufty velvety cord (8)
8 Nautical greeting (4)
9 One who estimates the cost of possessions (6)
10 Manner of speech (5)
11 Fronded plant (4)
12 Rip-off (3,5)
14 Covered by an awning (8)
18 Security device (4)
20 Cause of infection (5)
22 Gas (6)
23 ___ Spumante, fizzy wine (4)
24 Uneasily active (8)

DOWN

1 Short saying (6)
2 Veiled slur (8)
3 Church officer (6)
4 Friendly or harmless (6)
5 Vehicle available for hire (4)
6 Pertaining to the universe (6)
13 Plump (4-4)
15 Notify, inform (6)
16 Loose page or flyer in a magazine (6)
17 Invent, make (6)
19 One part of a meal (6)
21 Swift incursion (4)

Puzzle 179

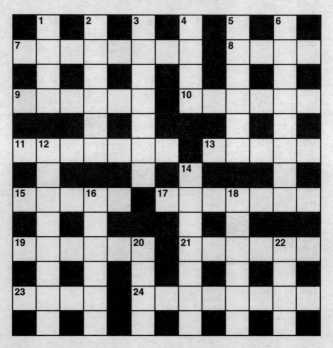

ACROSS

7 Lacking in value or merit (8)
8 Plant's underground part (4)
9 Unploughed field (6)
10 Advertising jingle (6)
11 Leave in the lurch (7)
13 Villain (5)
15 Coax (5)
17 Take the limelight from (7)
19 Coated, eg with silver (6)
21 Fruit-cake ingredient (6)
23 Biting insect (4)
24 Car safety device (4,4)

DOWN

1 Patella's location (4)
2 Made of precious metal (6)
3 Boiling pan (7)
4 Hooks and ___, fasteners (4)
5 Knight's suit (6)
6 Run unhurriedly (3,5)
12 Overhanging (brows) (8)
14 Austere (7)
16 Small and slim (6)
18 Soft felt hat (6)
20 Bowl (4)
22 In a lazy way (4)

Puzzle 180

ACROSS

6 Constructed to form a part of (2-5)
7 Disease of the glands (5)
9 Propel yourself through water (4)
10 Protesting, on foot (8)
11 Taps (6)
13 Derelict ship (4)
15 Quick cut (4)
16 Popular holiday area (6)
18 Less affluent (5,3)
21 Facebook function (4)
22 Light quick meal (5)
23 On fire (7)

DOWN

1 Wintry, white (5)
2 Muster, invoke (6,2)
3 Squalid overcrowded neighbourhood (4)
4 Of the same kind (4)
5 Lanky (7)
8 Emergency (6)
12 ___ dioxide, exhaled mixture (6)
13 Sport involving running and jumping (8)
14 Continuing (7)
17 Pelts (5)
19 Old coal container (4)
20 Continuous succession of changes (4)

Puzzle 181

ACROSS

1 Spryness (7)
5 Exploding device (4)
8 Fade (out) (5)
9 Bear no malice (7)
11 Garage incline (4)
12 Discharged from the army (8)
15 Animal's muzzle (5)
16 Blood channels (5)
19 Loafer (8)
21 Impure matter on the surface of a liquid (4)
23 Large cushion used as an informal low seat (7)
25 Passive (5)
26 Accidentally strike (your toe) (4)
27 Fruity bread roll (7)

DOWN

2 Soccer match proceeds (4,5)
3 Loiter in a sinister fashion (4)
4 Sweet made of sugar and butter (6)
5 Peaty ground (3)
6 Cinema film (5)
7 Glowing particle (5)
10 Person involved in violent disorder (6)
13 Teller, cashier (4,5)
14 Confused babble (6)
17 Gross mismanagement (6)
18 Metal worker (5)
20 Prevent (5)
22 Metallic element used in galvanising (4)
24 Central issue at the core of a problem (3)

Puzzle 182

ACROSS

1 Happening, brewing (5)
4 Moved up and down (6)
10 Felt-tipped writing implement (6,3)
11 Out of connection (3)
12 Radioactive (rays) (5)
13 Stand against (6)
14 Devotion of attention to your partner or child (7,4)
18 French high-kicking dance (6)
20 Bird with a red breast (5)
23 Possessed (3)
24 Engage in idle, pointless activity (4,5)
25 Mixed-up mess (6)
26 Being dishonest (5)

DOWN

2 Place of discussion (5)
3 Protective clothing (7)
5 Admit liability (3,2)
6 Come to fruition (7)
7 Nimble-fingered (4)
8 Likeness, mental picture (5)
9 Exploiting chances (11)
15 Having no assistance (7)
16 Raspy (7)
17 State of harmonious agreement (5)
19 Animal with humps (5)
21 Carried by the wind (5)
22 Mate (4)

Puzzle 183

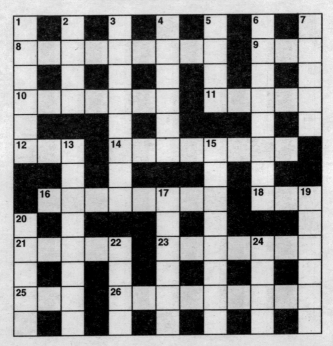

ACROSS

8 Prospector (4,5)
9 Pile on cloth (3)
10 Changeover period (7)
11 Winch (5)
12 Kept a date with (3)
14 Altruistic (8)
16 Enjoyable (8)
18 Archaeological site (3)
21 Fermented apple drink (5)
23 Breakable (7)
25 Unprocessed (3)
26 Autocratic manner (9)

DOWN

1 Concern solely for oneself (6)
2 Ink mark (4)
3 In classical mythology, food of the gods (8)
4 Creature (6)
5 Bridge's curved span (4)
6 Not prejudiced (8)
7 Malicious ill-will (5)
13 Belittle, underplay (4,4)
15 Wooden hut (3,5)
17 Instil, pervade (6)
19 Lubrication (6)
20 Musical arrangement (5)
22 Red gemstone (4)
24 Chilled (tea, eg) (4)

Puzzle 184

ACROSS

- **1** Food served alight (6)
- **4** Lupine animals (6)
- **9** Explain, solve (5,2)
- **10** Edition (5)
- **11** Peruvian animal (5)
- **12** Research-gathering (7)
- **13** Quickness, swiftness (5)
- **15** Half-melted snow (5)
- **20** Inclination (7)
- **22** High rank or character (5)
- **24** Group of fish (5)
- **25** Be a glutton (7)
- **26** End-of-term school document (6)
- **27** Tangled (6)

DOWN

- **1** Capricious (6)
- **2** Area of combat (5)
- **3** Quickfire series (of questions) (7)
- **5** Due for payment (5)
- **6** Thick and gluey (7)
- **7** Arab leader (6)
- **8** Drop (liquid) (5)
- **14** Leguminous broth (3,4)
- **16** Outside light (7)
- **17** More intimate (6)
- **18** Encourage (3,2)
- **19** With tenderness (6)
- **21** Lazy type (5)
- **23** Sheep's cry (5)

Puzzle 185

ACROSS

1 Sharp point (5)
4 Regular (5)
10 Respected person in a particular field (5)
11 In general (7)
12 Continue (5,2)
13 Bury (5)
14 Glue (5)
16 Be of the same mind (5)
21 Spanish open square (5)
23 Park wardens (7)
25 Dressed in a long cape (7)
26 Light fabric with a wrinkled surface (5)
27 Poisonous British snake (5)
28 Full of substance (5)

DOWN

2 Recompense (7)
3 Picture playing-cards (5)
5 Preserving over a fire (7)
6 Checking of accounts (5)
7 Change appropriately (5)
8 Choice steak (1-4)
9 Third gift of the Magi (5)
15 Make a sound like logs on a fire (7)
17 Essential factor (7)
18 Hot (food) (5)
19 Collective noun for lions (5)
20 Michaelmas daisy (5)
22 So as to be heard (5)
24 Recess (5)

Puzzle 186

ACROSS

1 Caller, guest (7)
5 Make advances (5)
8 Pronounce (5)
9 Raucous maritime bird (7)
10 Reticule (7)
12 Welsh canine (5)
14 Vigorously cleans (6)
16 Border (6)
18 Large solid box (5)
19 Upbraid (4,3)
22 Term of address expressing affection (3,4)
24 Jewish leader (5)
26 Raising agent used in baking (5)
27 Cloth, curtains (7)

DOWN

1 Assert, declare (5)
2 Take a pew (3)
3 Vibrate (5)
4 Abdicate (6)
5 Loose (7)
6 Note acknowledging a debt (inits) (3)
7 Mournfully ringing (7)
11 NHS worker (5)
13 Horned pachyderm (5)
14 Wages for ill employees (4,3)
15 Supporting role (3,4)
17 Wait upon (6)
20 Newly hatched insect (5)
21 Winged magical creature (5)
23 Afternoon meal (3)
25 Buzzing insect (3)

Puzzle 187

ACROSS

1 Extensively (6)
4 Grows (6)
8 Race (an engine) (3)
9 Without preparation (9)
11 Source of a river (4)
12 Electricity failure (8)
15 Neutral (9)
18 Attend (to) (8)
19 Rudely stare at (4)
21 Musical instrument originating in Trinidad (5,4)
23 Drag (3)
24 Stop from exploding (6)
25 Heavy, indigestible (6)

DOWN

1 Commendable, of merit (6)
2 Change, variance (9)
3 Wild beast's den (4)
5 Textured wallpaper (8)
6 Impudence (3)
7 Gushes (6)
10 Large white animal (5,4)
13 Bound, compelled (9)
14 Gospel preachers (8)
16 Caused mirth (6)
17 Elbow-room (6)
20 Give out or give off (4)
22 Gnome (3)

Puzzle 188

ACROSS

1 Fashions (6)
4 Drink that washes down another (6)
9 Envy, sloth, eg (6,3)
10 Assistance given to the needy (3)
11 Application (3)
12 Gems, treasures (9)
13 Smug look (5)
15 Telephone kiosk (5)
20 Trespassing (9)
22 Large area of salt water (3)
23 Trivial lie (3)
24 Proceed smoothly (4,5)
25 One-piece hosiery item (6)
26 Putrid (egg) (6)

DOWN

1 State of being wearisome (6)
2 Keep out of the way of (5)
3 Supply, give (7)
5 Reddish-brown dye (5)
6 ___ fever, infectious disease (7)
7 Hot salad vegetable (6)
8 Sacred song (5)
14 Post-sack (7)
16 Experienced performer (3,4)
17 Self-service light meal (6)
18 Boringly sober (5)
19 Frayed (6)
21 Be a guest (5)
22 Bobbin (5)

Puzzle 189

ACROSS

1 Paint and wallpaper a room (8)
6 Ambitions (5)
7 Audacity (4)
8 Aquatic plant (4)
9 Under the alternative name of (inits) (3)
10 Mountain's high point (4)
11 Tipster (6)
13 Vegetables, generally (6)
14 Robber, brigand (6)
17 Down-and-out, mendicant (6)
18 Pass the tongue over (something) (4)
20 Furthermore (3)
21 Sinfulness (4)
22 Outer limit (4)
23 Fine ground corn used in baking (5)
24 Observant (4-4)

DOWN

1 Excavate (3,2)
2 Picture made from scraps of fabric or paper (7)
3 Body powder (6)
4 Young herring (5)
5 Menacing attack (7)
6 Obstinately conservative person (4,3)
12 Half-suppressed laugh (7)
13 Delight (7)
15 Hang out after washing (4-3)
16 Spittle (6)
17 Anti-wrinkle drug (5)
19 Work (dough) (5)

Puzzle 190

ACROSS

1 Talks quietly into someone's ear (8)
5 Rabbit's tail (4)
9 Remarked (5)
10 Nocturnal bird with large eyes (4,3)
11 Loftily located (4)
12 Coloured paper thrown at weddings (8)
14 Prevented access (6)
15 Finale (6)
18 Workers' refreshment pause (3,5)
20 Part of speech which can be active or passive (4)
22 Back complaint (7)
23 Go one better than (5)
24 Become old-fashioned (4)
25 Hiker's luggage item (8)

DOWN

1 Helicopter's lifting device (5)
2 Whole number (7)
3 Small thin cushion (3)
4 Decorative strip of cloth (6)
6 Hit or influence (5)
7 Farming (7)
8 Obscene (7)
13 Cardboard coaster (4,3)
14 Preserved in jars (7)
16 Force preventing movement (7)
17 Chinese tower temple (6)
19 Concede (5)
21 Impede (5)
23 Acorn tree (3)

Puzzle 191

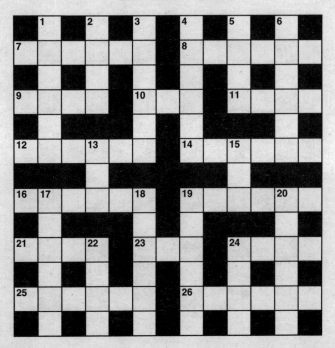

ACROSS

7 Division of a shop or business (6)
8 Legless grub of a fly (6)
9 Person who studies too hard (4)
10 Chinese cooking pan (3)
11 Oil platforms (4)
12 Web weaver (6)
14 Watercourses (6)
16 Liaison (6)
19 Watch out! (6)
21 Paradise (4)
23 Pistol or rifle, eg (3)
24 Yarn woven across the width of the fabric (4)
25 Acid's opposite (6)
26 Sufficiently (6)

DOWN

1 Reach a level of maturity (4,2)
2 Make (a woollen garment) using needles (4)
3 Short period of rain (6)
4 One who consumes cigarettes (6)
5 Food thickener from seaweed (4)
6 Maker of counterfeit money (6)
13 Main component of chromosomes (inits) (3)
15 Solemn promise (3)
17 Dishonest scheme (6)
18 Acquire anew (6)
19 Loud firework (6)
20 Safe house (6)
22 Clean, orderly and tidy in appearance (4)
24 Fleece (4)

Puzzle 192

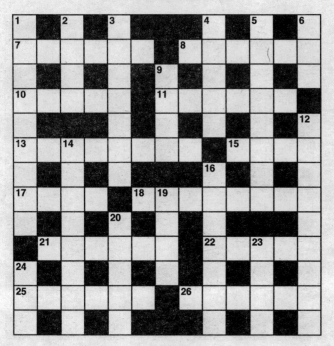

ACROSS

7 Breathe out (6)
8 Piece of jewellery (6)
10 Enter into combat (5)
11 New group (of pupils) (6)
13 Frankly, between chaps (3,2,3)
15 Firmly against (4)
17 Accrue (4)
18 Merry-go-round (8)
21 Worshipped (6)
22 On no occasion (5)
25 Needlework (6)
26 Short Spanish jacket (6)

DOWN

1 Conception of your abilities (4-5)
2 Brutal lout (4)
3 High spirits (7)
4 Thick soup made with meat and vegetables (5)
5 Record of calculations (8)
6 Question word answered by 'because' (3)
9 City founded by Pizarro in 1535 (4)
12 Shade of red (6-3)
14 Fix permanently (4,4)
16 Have reason to expect (5,2)
19 Diplomatic assistant (4)
20 Go to press (5)
23 Aspect (4)
24 Put questions to (3)

Puzzle 193

ACROSS

1 Brownish-yellow pigment (6)
8 Lorry-driving (8)
9 Slothful (4)
10 Speak in a slow lengthened tone (5)
11 Earth's satellite (4)
12 Laundry stiffening product (6)
14 Travelling (6)
16 One who has left his or her native country (6)
19 Hearth surround (6)
21 Fore of a ship (4)
23 Trace, smattering (5)
25 Craving (4)
26 Attack wildly (3,3,2)
27 Thick dairy product with a sour taste (6)

DOWN

2 Admit (to an organisation) (6)
3 Requisite (4)
4 Add, append (6)
5 Hairdresser's tube (6)
6 Remove from the surface (4)
7 Hereditary (6)
13 Floor mat (3)
15 French word for 'wine' (3)
17 Border (6)
18 Property (6)
19 Out of order, defective (6)
20 Any of two (6)
22 Small forest (4)
24 Fall, drape (4)

Puzzle 194

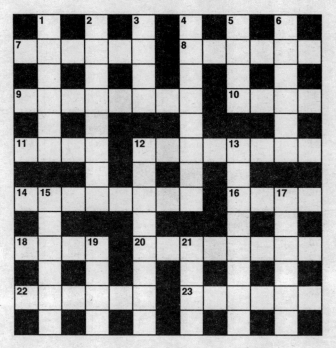

ACROSS

7 Not bought (6)
8 Esoteric (6)
9 Poisoned (8)
10 Mania, craze (4)
11 Move slowly on a runway (4)
12 One who lives off others and contributes nothing (8)
14 Gesture (a vehicle) to stop (4,4)
16 Spick and span (4)
18 Pleased with yourself! (4)
20 Wrapper for a letter (8)
22 Dark blue dye (6)
23 Well-baked, or crabby (6)

DOWN

1 Variety of wool from a goat or a rabbit (6)
2 Prone to flooding? (3-5)
3 Abridge (a text) (4)
4 Approach (a certain state) (6,2)
5 Mark of an old wound (4)
6 Plant disease caused by fungi (6)
12 Public facility for making calls (5,3)
13 Pay (6,2)
15 Citrus fruits (6)
17 Stand-in, proxy (6)
19 Way of walking (4)
21 Tool for gripping (4)

Puzzle 195

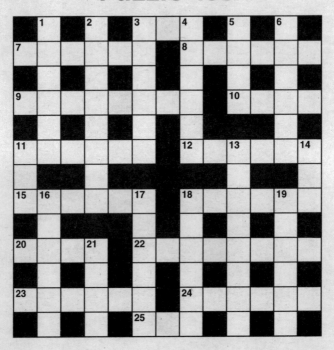

ACROSS

3 Psychic power (inits) (3)
7 Considerate (6)
8 Time-telling word (6)
9 Rope tie that may be undone with a pull (4,4)
10 Unprocessed paper (4)
11 Confronting (6)
12 Downgrade, reduce in rank (6)
15 Hot spice (6)
18 Quick answer (6)
20 Far from brand-new (4)
22 Unorthodox person (8)
23 Word form when talking about more than one (6)
24 Justification (6)
25 Centre of a storm (3)

DOWN

1 Spanish fish and chicken dish (6)
2 Quivering (muscles) (8)
3 Warm yellow drink containing sherry or brandy (3-3)
4 Scored at snooker (6)
5 Debacle (4)
6 Make a statue (6)
11 Cloud at ground level (3)
13 Fabric, cloth (8)
14 Devour (3)
16 Rude remark (6)
17 Unwanted fold (6)
18 Venerate, worship (6)
19 Member of the clergy (6)
21 Filth (4)

Puzzle 196

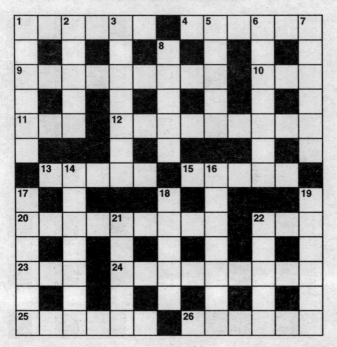

ACROSS

1 Long cream cake (6)
4 Unit used when measuring temperature (6)
9 Lessens, reduces (9)
10 Colour artificially (3)
11 Quantity of money (3)
12 Cords for tying footwear (9)
13 Suspended playground seat (5)
15 Happy rustic scene (5)
20 Without a stitch on (2,3,4)
22 Rayburn-like cooker (3)
23 Go downhill fast on snow (3)
24 Finds (new lands, eg) (9)
25 Small lump of gold (6)
26 Pour through a sieve (6)

DOWN

1 Most advanced in years (6)
2 Doctor called in to cover for another (5)
3 Bread roll with a sugary glaze (4,3)
5 Artist's picture support (5)
6 Revolutionary (7)
7 Yet, all the same (4,2)
8 Preclude, in legal terms (5)
14 Soaking (7)
16 Clean out (a refrigerator) (7)
17 ___ hut, corrugated iron shelter (6)
18 Witch's spell (5)
19 Rector, vicar (6)
21 Provide with (5)
22 Betel-nut tree (5)

Puzzle 197

ACROSS

1 Discard, throw overboard (8)
6 Gently mountainous (5)
7 Mob uprising (4)
8 Sound bounce (4)
9 ___ Healy, Irish singer/songwriter (3)
10 Balkan aniseed-flavoured spirit (4)
11 Gave a clue (6)
13 Trendy, fashionable (4,2)
14 Damaged, faulty (6)
17 Work hard (6)
18 Snatch hold of (4)
20 Hawaiian floral garland (3)
21 Corner, narrow recess (4)
22 Went by plane (4)
23 Sound of elastic breaking (5)
24 Imagined (8)

DOWN

1 One of twelve in court (5)
2 Set of spanners, screwdrivers etc (4,3)
3 Exotic flower (6)
4 Fluffy or feathery sky feature (5)
5 Spun round (7)
6 Youth ___, places to stay (7)
12 Prevaricating (7)
13 Small folding cases for money (7)
15 Sings like a bird (7)
16 Popular number puzzle (6)
17 Mauve-flowered shrub (5)
19 Inclined the head as a sign of respect (5)

Puzzle 198

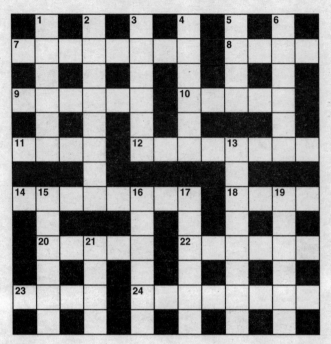

ACROSS

7 Chains (8)
8 Musical composition (4)
9 Summer shoe (6)
10 Guardian spirit (5)
11 Brush the surface (4)
12 Dirt guards (8)
14 Obstructing (8)
18 Affectionate peck (4)
20 Pub spirit measure (5)
22 Excavation (6)
23 Join (metals) (4)
24 Government office (8)

DOWN

1 Contracted (6)
2 Educational (8)
3 Skiing event (6)
4 Sea-bound area (6)
5 Yearn, pine (4)
6 Out of space (4,2)
13 Copy, replica (8)
15 Set free or undo (6)
16 Wages, salary (6)
17 Casino activity (6)
19 Soldier on guard (6)
21 Spick and span (4)

Puzzle 199

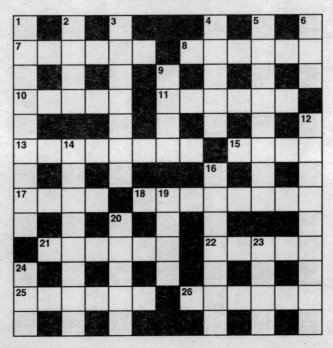

ACROSS

7 Under threat, in danger (2,4)
8 Notify (6)
10 Ship's steadying anchor (5)
11 Belgium's continent (6)
13 Spotting, seeing (8)
15 Ancient Japanese form of wrestling (4)
17 Hard part of a toe (4)
18 Backed (8)
21 Magic potion (6)
22 Direction of the Arctic Circle (5)
25 Cows (6)
26 Gathered from a tree (6)

DOWN

1 Growing gloomy (9)
2 Barren, parched (4)
3 Vital extract (7)
4 Force air through the nostrils like a horse (5)
5 Frothy bubbles (8)
6 Electrical unit (3)
9 Type of mathematical diagram (4)
12 Huts for storing timber (9)
14 Three babies born together (8)
16 Canadian police officer on horseback (7)
19 Expected standard (4)
20 Banish abroad (5)
23 Lawn-tidying tool (4)
24 Top playing-card (3)

Puzzle 200

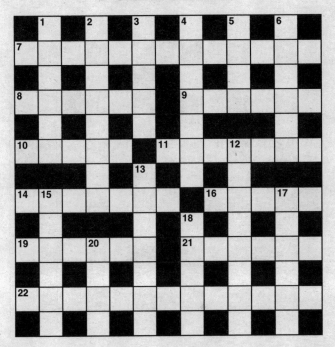

ACROSS

7 Member of a workers' syndicate (5,8)
8 Ornamental spiral (6)
9 Bird or plant preserved in rock (6)
10 Local authority edict (5)
11 Upgrade (7)
14 Unknown person (7)
16 Gradient, incline (5)
19 Operating an aircraft (6)
21 Just a moment! (4,2)
22 With premeditation (13)

DOWN

1 Dear, costly (6)
2 Person who intercedes on behalf of another (8)
3 Water-cut channel in rock (5)
4 Of a plan, go awry (7)
5 Industrious insects (4)
6 Casual or sports garment (1-5)
12 Dense fruity bread (4,4)
13 Chessmen (7)
15 Connected by broadband (6)
17 Inadequately (6)
18 Vibrated (5)
20 Chilled (4)

Puzzle 201

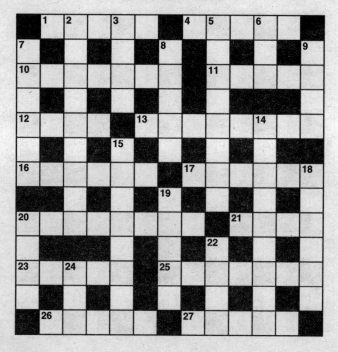

ACROSS

1 *Beauty and the* ___, fairy tale (5)
4 Black hardwood (5)
10 Cook by immersing in hot oil (4-3)
11 Pertaining to a style from the past (5)
12 Formal test (4)
13 At the end of the line, done for (6-2)
16 Head journalist (6)
17 Boy's singing voice (6)
20 Irksome, vexatious (8)
21 Injure with a knife (4)
23 Latin-American dance (5)
25 Confidentiality (7)
26 No longer sleeping (5)
27 Investigation (5)

DOWN

2 Side or face of a building (9)
3 Use a riddle (4)
5 Graph with blocks (3,5)
6 Word that makes a sentence negative (3)
7 Remain attached (6)
8 Obscure or secluded path (5)
9 Hen enclosure (4)
14 Payment method (5,4)
15 Hackneyed (8)
18 Beginning of a baby (6)
19 Unskilful (5)
20 Creative (4)
22 Handle of a sword (4)
24 Without delay (3)

Puzzle 202

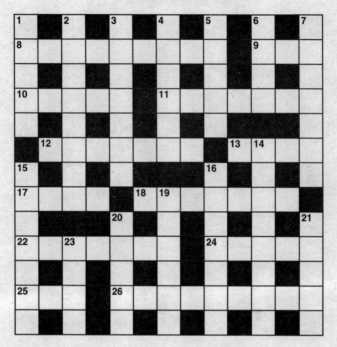

ACROSS

8 Pretended, faked (9)
9 Since (3)
10 Escape (5)
11 Make a fuss of (7)
12 Detailed location (7)
13 Polluted air (4)
17 Folklore giant (4)
18 Poisonous (7)
22 Thoughtful-looking (7)
24 Appellation (5)
25 Forty winks (3)
26 Degree of pomp (9)

DOWN

1 Article of value (5)
2 Burn slowly without a flame (8)
3 Mathematical system (7)
4 Openings in country walls (6)
5 Device for storing digital information (1,1-3)
6 Eastern garment (4)
7 Diamond shape or medicated sweet (7)
14 Very large hill (8)
15 Surface layer on a pizza (7)
16 Be inopportune at (7)
19 Excessively (6)
20 Wash off soap (5)
21 Blue-green gemstone (5)
23 Scruff of the neck (4)

Puzzle 203

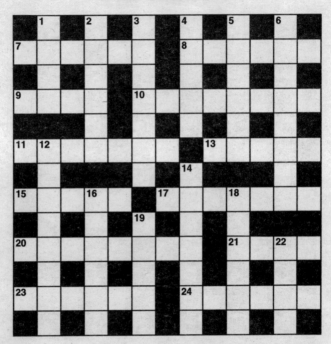

ACROSS

7 Flesh of sheep (6)
8 Stradivarius instrument (6)
9 Sudden sharp pain (4)
10 Variety of currant bun (4,4)
11 As a rule (7)
13 Solemn (5)
15 Restless, fidgety (5)
17 Sweaters, pullovers (7)
20 Waste bag for household rubbish (3-5)
21 Just about manage (4)
23 Is expected to (6)
24 Owner's assets minus liabilities (6)

DOWN

1 Distinctive air (4)
2 Sign of social disapproval (6)
3 Very crossly (7)
4 Remove (from a building) (5)
5 Football (6)
6 Run slowly, idle (4,4)
12 Stay put and wait it out (3,5)
14 One fourth (7)
16 Gas that is lighter than air (6)
18 Finish work at the end of the day (4,2)
19 Derogatory in a supercilious way (5)
22 Hit a golf ball into the hole (4)

Puzzle 204

ACROSS

1 Method of carrying a person (8,4)
9 Musical drama such as Carmen (5)
10 Fête game (7)
11 Long-standing family
employee (8)
12 Traditional story (4)
14 Pandemonium (6)
15 Motorist (6)
18 Run in slow strides (4)
20 Tarnish (8)
23 Unit of sound measurement (7)
24 Neck pain (5)
25 Molecular structure (12)

DOWN

2 With an utter lack of ability (7)
3 Test-setter (8)
4 Deer horn (6)
5 Oil reserve in an engine (4)
6 Elephant's tusk material (5)
7 Class instructor (7)
8 Quartet (4)
13 Choice piece of meat (5,3)
14 Making an agreeable sound (7)
16 Loss of balance (7)
17 Piece of small shot (6)
19 Nut variety (5)
21 Long walk (4)
22 Aid (a criminal) (4)

Puzzle 205

ACROSS

1 Short zipped coat (6,6)
9 Heavy road transport (7)
10 Bottomless gulf (5)
11 Fat used to make puddings (4)
12 Apparent (7)
15 Natural fibre (6)
16 Suitable for both genders (6)
19 Concise, often ironic saying or poem (7)
21 Sinful (4)
24 Portable light (5)
25 Doubly (7)
26 Medical establishment (6,6)

DOWN

2 Lavish (7)
3 Small pierced ball hung on a necklace (4)
4 Bailiffs, historically (6)
5 Shocking, frightening (8)
6 Enter (data) on a computer (3,2)
7 Chore (4)
8 Study of matter and energy (7)
13 Wild guess or venture (4,4)
14 Burst (7)
17 Liberator (7)
18 Strategy, plan (6)
20 Furry anorak with a hood (5)
22 Firmly mark (4)
23 Official robe (4)

Puzzle 206

ACROSS

1 Sudden increase (5)
4 Gigantic (7)
9 Silver-screen celebrity (4,4)
10 Large cymbal (4)
11 Adage (6)
12 Metal plating (6)
13 Fund-raising gathering over a hot drink (6,7)
17 Make fun of (4,2)
19 Just short of (6)
21 Hindu queen (4)
22 Become less amusing over time (4,4)
23 Vivid figures of speech (7)
24 Sprightly (5)

DOWN

2 ___ to, familiar with (5)
3 Interlude from work (4,3)
5 Country bordering Algeria (7)
6 Raring to go (5)
7 Sleep-bringer in folklore (7)
8 Collar fastener (4)
14 Style of bowling (7)
15 Permit someone to do something (7)
16 ID badge (4,3)
18 Carrying out (5)
19 At a distance (4)
20 Gyrate (5)

Puzzle 207

ACROSS

1 Female sovereign (7)
4 Adept (4)
9 Wild fruit that is very high in vitamin C (7)
11 Furious (5)
12 Artery that carries blood from the heart (5)
13 Placed in a catalogue (6)
15 Egg on (6)
17 Colouring pencil (6)
19 Patriotic song (6)
20 Provoke (5)
23 Steam bath invented in Finland (5)
24 Vote in again (2-5)
25 Contest for two (4)
26 Person pedalling along (7)

DOWN

2 Person who hoards money (5)
3 Pliant, lithe (6)
5 Fearlessness (7)
6 Stares at (4)
7 Illegal entry (5-2)
8 Professed respect (3,7)
10 Direct contest between two people (4-2-4)
14 Falsity (7)
16 Rebuke (7)
18 Fawning, obsequious (6)
21 Board-game with pawns and rooks (5)
22 Pre-owned, second-hand (4)

Puzzle 208

ACROSS

1 Level, not bumpy (6)
4 Implicit (5)
8 Ransack (5)
9 Affect, involve (7)
10 (Of a couple) separate (5,2)
11 Spoken language exam (4)
12 And the rest (abbrev.) (3)
14 Surface layer (4)
15 Biscuit for baby to chew (4)
18 Natural energy (3)
21 Pelvic bones (4)
23 Stowers (7)
25 Hit with an open hand (7)
26 Go in (5)
27 Childminder (5)
28 Erring (6)

DOWN

1 Disco light (6)
2 Time of cheap-rate electricity (3-4)
3 Journeying on foot (8)
4 Small (4)
5 Unobstructed (5)
6 Causing a prickly sensation (6)
7 Extent (5)
13 Noisy grasshopper-like insects (8)
16 Feel very hot (7)
17 Singled out (6)
19 Shovel (5)
20 Fish hawk (6)
22 Shellfish (5)
24 Active, nimble (4)

Puzzle 209

ACROSS

7 Taunting (8)
8 Revolve rapidly (4)
10 Spicy sausage (7)
11 Guide for drawing lines (5)
12 Hard-shelled seeds (4)
13 Fix, put right (7)
16 Flabbergast (7)
18 Small car or skirt (4)
22 Refuge (5)
24 Raise (a matter) for discussion (5,2)
25 Pillar in a fence (4)
26 Veteran (3-5)

DOWN

1 More than probable (4-2)
2 Squaddies (8)
3 Mature person (5)
4 Catalyst present in some modern washing powders (6)
5 Off-white gem (4)
6 Loud breath when asleep (5)
9 Foamy mass of air bubbles (5)
14 Legitimate object for attack (4,4)
15 Hurt, injure (5)
17 Take small bites, like a mouse (6)
19 Bring into the country (6)
20 French fries (5)
21 Dirt (5)
23 Huge (4)

Puzzle 210

ACROSS

7 Pleasure-seeking male (7)
8 Fossilised tree resin (5)
9 Free (of) (3)
10 Ooze out (5)
11 Haul (3)
12 For all to see (6)
14 Look angrily (6)
16 Aboard ship (6)
17 Salvo of gunfire (6)
19 Unwell (3)
21 Baptised (5)
23 Unit of genetic material (inits) (3)
24 Impish (5)
25 Jewelled head decoration (7)

DOWN

1 Forceful pitch (4,4)
2 Reed instrument (4)
3 Sweet thick liquid (5)
4 London station (8)
5 Have a common boundary with (4)
6 Substance used in beer-making (7,5)
7 Custom-made for an individual (12)
13 Education (8)
15 Thoroughly cooked (4-4)
18 Loose protective garment worn by artists (5)
20 Raise up (4)
22 Patch up (socks) (4)

Puzzle 211

ACROSS

1 Extreme (5)
4 Unclear (7)
9 Diverse assortment (5,3)
10 Rhythm (4)
11 Yes-man (6)
12 Person penning a book (6)
13 Quarter of a whole (6)
16 Have a discussion (6)
18 Writing implement (6)
20 Call in (4,2)
22 Drag a leg when walking (4)
23 Example, case in point (8)
24 Hypodermic (7)
25 Work shift (5)

DOWN

2 Articles of porcelain (5)
3 Intrepid marcher (7)
5 Looking ill and exhausted (7)
6 First appearance (5)
7 Make threadbare (4,3)
8 Competently (4)
14 Corpulence (7)
15 Aiding (7)
17 Cheerful and optimistic (7)
19 Bay of Naples isle (5)
20 Start of nightfall (4)
21 Pork product (5)

Puzzle 212

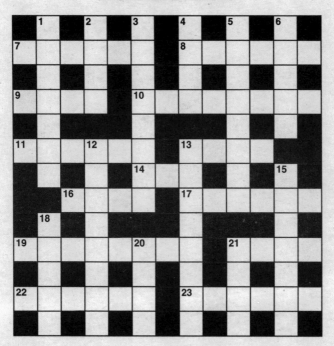

ACROSS

7 Martial art practised by Bruce Lee (4,2)
8 Straight away (2,4)
9 Slang term for 'potato' (4)
10 Gets denser (8)
11 Small food shopkeeper (6)
13 Rescue from harm (4)
14 Rough-leaved tall tree (3)
16 Give temporarily (4)
17 Task involving a short journey (6)
19 Drop rapidly from a plane (4-4)
21 Fondness, affection (4)
22 Joining process (6)
23 Agreeably (6)

DOWN

1 Evening meals (7)
2 Grew older (4)
3 Spoke indistinctly (8)
4 Island east of Java (4)
5 Gained control of (4,4)
6 Location (in a film) (5)
12 Place to eat French pancakes (8)
13 Giving off an aroma (8)
15 Blubbers, whimpers (7)
18 Monetary deception (5)
20 Female relative (4)
21 Success due to chance (4)

Puzzle 213

ACROSS

6 Poignant, evocative (8)
8 Talk to a deity (4)
10 Eagle's hooked 'foot' (5)
11 Desert burrowing rodent (6)
13 Inevitable destiny (4)
14 Recovers from a wreck (8)
16 Orating (8)
19 Calf's meat (4)
22 Air travellers' ailment (3,3)
23 Punched metal fastener (5)
25 Injure by rough handling or clawing (4)
26 Tightly fought (5-3)

DOWN

1 Cod, haddock etc (5,4)
2 Hard seed in a peach (5)
3 Mystery (6)
4 Attempting (6)
5 Exercise room (3)
7 In darkness (5)
9 Went by car (5)
12 Detaching (9)
15 Move furtively (5)
17 Make equal, balance out (4,2)
18 Trivial complaint (6)
20 Young eel (5)
21 Bumptious, cocky (5)
24 Shortened form of the SI unit of current (3)

Puzzle 214

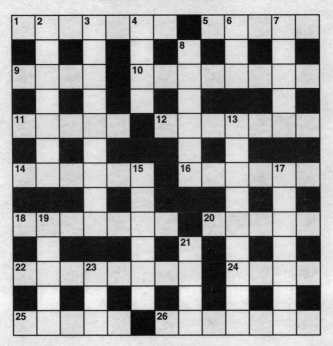

ACROSS

1 Shipping hazard in cold regions (7)
5 Hotel providing spa treatments (5)
9 Complimentary (4)
10 Area of radio frequencies (4,4)
11 Stony, craggy (5)
12 Ceremonious, stately (7)
14 Piece pared off (6)
16 Put in a box (6)
18 Relating to adolescents (7)
20 Thin mortar used between tiles (5)
22 Mimic (8)
24 Public houses (4)
25 Daring feat (5)
26 Unit of troops (7)

DOWN

2 Arrangement to share lifts to work (3-4)
3 Reach a point where profits are equal to costs (5,4)
4 Irritate (4)
6 Tree commonly found in a graveyard (3)
7 Noisy celebration (5)
8 No person in particular (6)
13 Happening repeatedly (9)
15 Style of sleeve that is joined to the neckband (6)
17 Staggered (7)
19 Be alive (5)
21 Go off at a tangent (4)
23 Grecian vessel? (3)

Puzzle 215

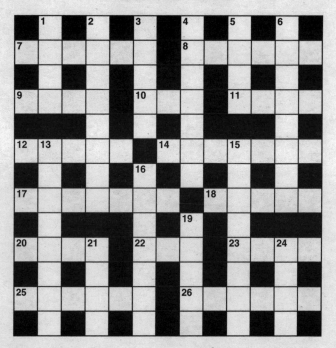

ACROSS

7 Lively and cheerful (6)
8 Wait, be patient (4,2)
9 Small stinging insect (4)
10 Glossy fabric (inits) (3)
11 Erase (the content) from tape (4)
12 Inuit snow-hut (5)
14 Room for books (7)
17 In eager haste (7)
18 News-stand (5)
20 Pang (4)
22 Pastry-based dish (3)
23 Cold and musty (4)
25 Blubber, whine (6)
26 Garment worn with a dinner jacket (3,3)

DOWN

1 Lowest part of the face (4)
2 Something damaged beyond repair (5-3)
3 Mythological female divinity (5)
4 Announce your arrival at a hotel (5,2)
5 Be aware (4)
6 Likens (8)
13 Cementing (8)
15 Fall from above in large amounts (4,4)
16 Collect (7)
19 Match between local teams (5)
21 Group (of beautiful girls) (4)
24 Metal spike (4)

Puzzle 216

ACROSS

1 Image made from glass fragments (6)
5 Light fog (4)
8 Quick profit (1,4,4)
9 Under the alternative name of (inits) (3)
11 Assignment (4)
12 Fellow employee (2-6)
14 Nut used in marzipan (6)
16 Senior university lecturer (6)
18 Element formerly called wolfram (8)
19 Ankle-length garment (4)
22 Decay (3)
23 Keyboard character consisting of an oblique line (9)
24 Family ___, chart showing relationships (4)
25 Suffer death or ruin (6)

DOWN

2 Iridescent gemstones (5)
3 Ostentatiously creative (4)
4 Token, ticket (6)
5 Complete transformation (8)
6 Hunted (7)
7 Thoroughly proficient person (4,6)
10 Cargo sent by plane (3,7)
13 Out of service (8)
15 Gigantic creature (7)
17 Container for a beverage (6)
20 Heap up, collect (5)
21 Russian ruler (4)

Puzzle 217

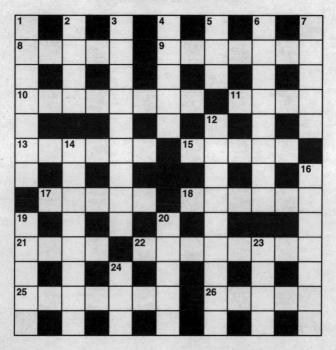

ACROSS

8 Lines from the centre to the edge of circles (5)
9 Large glass (7)
10 Miner's work area (4-4)
11 Absorbent cotton pad (4)
13 Domino ___, knock-on result (6)
15 Cut (meat) (5)
17 Bore (a hole) (5)
18 Commotion (6)
21 Emblem of Wales (4)
22 Punctuation mark at the end of a sentence (4,4)
25 Meat from the chest of a cow (7)
26 Volley (5)

DOWN

1 Commonest British fern (7)
2 Notion (4)
3 Problematic (9)
4 Large orderly pile of hay (5)
5 Australian flightless bird (3)
6 Be quietly forgotten (4,4)
7 Corrupt offer (5)
12 Perfect (9)
14 Escape route in case of a blaze (4,4)
16 Medical sign (7)
19 ___ artichoke, vegetable (5)
20 Glazier's sealant (5)
23 Tax for using a road (4)
24 Bright shade of blue (3)

Puzzle 218

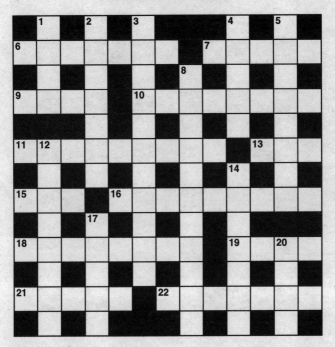

ACROSS

6 Stratum just below the surface of the ground (7)
7 Bicycle accessories (5)
9 Elegant (4)
10 Celtic dance (5,3)
11 Mournful (9)
13 Money dispenser (inits) (3)
15 Flow away (3)
16 Hunters (9)
18 Wall writings (8)
19 Exotic fruit (4)
21 Dismal (5)
22 Obtain by buying (7)

DOWN

1 Quieten (4)
2 Clairvoyant, spiritualist (7)
3 Feeling of chill (3,2,3,3)
4 Pulpy (5)
5 Runner (8)
8 Tree with pale peeling bark (6,5)
12 People who believe in tolerance and progress (8)
14 Shock (5,2)
17 Edible waste parts of a carcase (5)
20 Slender but strong (4)

Puzzle 219

ACROSS

1 Opposite aspect (4,4)
5 Large-scale (4)
8 Ugly yet tasty sea creature (8)
9 Door fixture (4)
11 Inanimate stage object (4)
12 Provide new accommodation for (7)
14 Temporarily (6)
16 Group of lines in a long poem (6)
18 Stimulated (7)
19 General idea (4)
22 Covered with fondant (4)
23 Cataleptic (8)
24 Requiring little effort (4)
25 Immovable (8)

DOWN

1 Emit smoke (4)
2 Underlying (5)
3 Area of the mouth (4,6)
4 Render harmless or beguile (6)
6 Black and white flightless seabird (7)
7 Funicular (5-3)
10 Snapshot (10)
13 Evader of government charges (3,5)
15 Illegal users of computer systems (7)
17 Connect to (6)
20 Astound (5)
21 Rest sideways (4)

Puzzle 220

ACROSS

1 Usefully (11)
8 Foreign Office diplomat (6)
9 Quality of being extremely thorough (6)
10 Home of a nursery-rhyme old woman (4)
11 High collar on a jumper (4,4)
13 Open space in a forest (5)
15 OT song (5)
18 Set apart (8)
19 Burning part of a candle (4)
20 Officially authorised (6)
21 Undeniably (6)
22 Uncomfortably near (remark) (5,2,4)

DOWN

2 Mountain's lower slopes (9)
3 Happen next (5)
4 Spring flowers (6)
5 Manly (6)
6 Traditional tales (7)
7 Hard journey (4)
12 Moisturiser (4,5)
14 Glum, miserable (7)
16 Equipment for walking tall (6)
17 Unmoored (6)
18 Lazily (4)
19 Distance across a swimming pool (5)

Puzzle 221

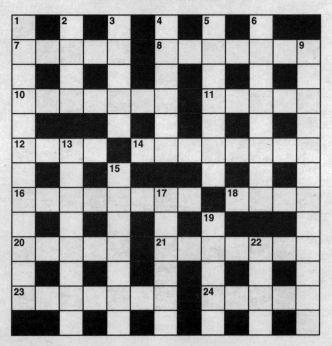

ACROSS

7 Turnips, in Scotland (5)
8 Raucous cry (7)
10 Flatter, cajole (7)
11 Strongly flavoured dark brown coffee (5)
12 Period in cricket (4)
14 Person attempting to get away from it all (8)
16 Noisy shaking (8)
18 High-priced (4)
20 Non-reactive (5)
21 Admit to having committed an offence (7)
23 Set sail (2,2,3)
24 Binding of a book (5)

DOWN

1 Winter sport (12)
2 Unit of DNA (4)
3 Words spoken directly to a theatre audience (5)
4 Test (6)
5 Structure of a language (7)
6 See (8)
9 Spa town (6,6)
13 Petition (8)
15 Favouring of a select group (7)
17 Sweet liquid (6)
19 Rap at a door (5)
22 Green emotion? (4)

Puzzle 222

ACROSS

7 Excessively tempting (12)
9 Area of high level ground (7)
10 Basic Italian food (5)
11 Cotton holder (4)
12 Defending soccer player (4,4)
14 At a disadvantage (5,3)
17 Cram for exams (4)
20 Square root of 64 (5)
21 Innovation (7)
23 Bulk manufactured (4-8)

DOWN

1 Thin strand (4)
2 Produce (6)
3 Residue of a fire (5)
4 Convince (6)
5 Argue or argument (7)
6 Colourless part of blood (6)
8 Emporium (6)
11 Hydrophobia (6)
13 Examination at the optician's (3,4)
15 Soldier's identification disc (3,3)
16 Most elegant clothes (6)
18 Pitiable person (6)
19 Native of Gothenburg, perhaps (5)
22 Sporting team (4)

Puzzle 223

ACROSS

8 Disparaged (7)
9 Wild yellow and white flower (5)
10 Fundamental (5)
11 Cook too much (6)
13 Use, utilise (6)
15 Spicy meat product (6)
17 Turn the radio on to a particular station (4,2)
18 Silenced (6)
20 Bathroom fitment (6)
22 Fish of the carp family (5)
25 Stay longer than expected (5)
26 Adviser (7)

DOWN

1 'Best before' indication (3-2,4)
2 Trainee reporters (4)
3 Vegetable of the cabbage family (8)
4 Append (3,2)
5 Work-shy (4)
6 Avian drinking and washing basin (4-4)
7 Word of farewell (3)
12 Additional factor cooling the weather (4,5)
14 Black leopards (8)
16 In zodiacal terms, the Water Bearer (8)
19 Fissure, gap (5)
21 Techniques (4)
23 As well (4)
24 Dined (3)

Puzzle 224

ACROSS

1 Egyptian goddess of fertility (4)
4 Winner's badge of ribbon (7)
8 Japanese dwarf tree (6)
9 Public speaker (6)
10 Housing (horses) (8)
12 Visual organs (4)
13 Breed of goat yielding long silky wool (6)
15 Sample cutting of material (6)
17 Coagulate (4)
19 In the altogether (8)
21 Be sure of (4,2)
22 Call in, visit (4,2)
24 Dealt with (7)
25 Hang on to (4)

DOWN

2 Abbreviate (7)
3 Distress signal (inits) (3)
4 Alternative healing technique (5)
5 Scapegoats (7)
6 Brand label (9)
7 Flee with the intent to marry (5)
11 Gift voucher for a keen reader (4,5)
14 Factory or storehouse for weaponry (7)
16 Responsive to treatment (7)
18 Dog strap (5)
20 Joined on (5)
23 Hardwood (3)

Puzzle 225

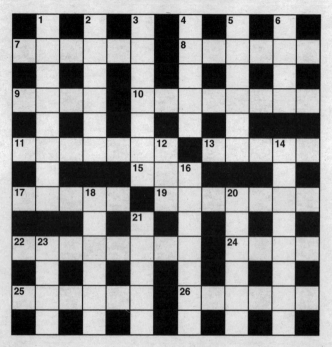

ACROSS

7 Two-piece costume (6)
8 Professional reviewer (6)
9 Zilch (4)
10 Drawings (8)
11 Noise of artillery (7)
13 Woodland fairy (5)
15 Small dog's bark (3)
17 Hair on a man's chin (5)
19 Abrading (7)
22 Swapped (goods) (8)
24 Wheedle (4)
25 Filtered (6)
26 Australian animal (6)

DOWN

1 Paid job without duties (8)
2 Informed hint (3-3)
3 Farm for porkers (7)
4 Clear off! (5)
5 Strong (6)
6 Bluish-white metallic element used in alloys (4)
12 Blade of corn (3)
14 Small police vehicle (5,3)
16 Humiliate (3,4)
18 Spin round (6)
20 Suit, adorn fittingly (6)
21 Overly moral person (5)
23 Very dry (4)

Puzzle 226

ACROSS

1 Reach, attain (7)
5 Elliptic shapes (5)
8 Body part affected by gingivitis (3)
9 Crockery and cutlery (9)
10 Garment worn by ancient Romans (4)
11 Hated, loathed (8)
14 Barrel maker (6)
15 Work (6)
17 Disconcerted (8)
18 Floating waste matter (4)
21 Rack with pegs for hanging outer garments (4-5)
23 Indisposed (3)
24 Entertaining tales (5)
25 Geometrical figure with three or more sides (7)

DOWN

1 Psychological unease (5)
2 Produced locally (4-5)
3 Dines (4)
4 Symbol of a country or organisation (6)
5 Attach undue importance to (8)
6 Under the alternative name of (inits) (3)
7 Thin, lean (7)
12 Lolling, sagging (9)
13 Obsession, phobia (8)
14 Noisy to chew (7)
16 Make off secretly (6)
19 Fruit often served as a starter (5)
20 Object of adoration (4)
22 Broadcast (3)

Puzzle 227

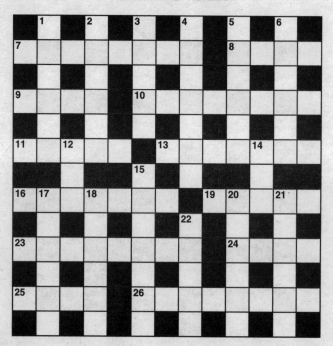

ACROSS

7 Dark orange-brown (5,3)
8 Encrusted with sugar (4)
9 Radiate (4)
10 Species grown indoors (3,5)
11 Mammary gland of a cow (5)
13 Orator's platform (7)
16 Glancing (7)
19 Resembling a snake's skin (5)
23 Uncontrolled movement of cattle (8)
24 The Big ___, nickname for New Orleans (4)
25 Set fire to (4)
26 Offering guidance (8)

DOWN

1 Encased (a picture) (6)
2 Old reaping tool (6)
3 Fruit used in making wine (5)
4 Copies of a book published at one time (7)
5 Replenish (4,2)
6 Adjoining shed (4-2)
12 Twosome (3)
14 Lingerie item (3)
15 Essential safety protection for Rollerbladers (4-3)
17 Leave behind thanks to superior speed (6)
18 Japanese gown (6)
20 ___ and onion, flavour of crisps (6)
21 Gloss (6)
22 Interlace (5)

Puzzle 228

ACROSS

1 Spider's snare (6)
4 Tie up (an animal) (6)
9 Time-waster (5)
10 Mental abstraction (7)
11 Soft leather from a goat-like animal (7)
12 Yellow of an egg (4)
14 Flecked (6)
16 Bend at speed (6)
19 Abrupt rough movement (4)
21 Sore (7)
24 Strive (7)
25 Cutting tool (5)
26 Set of ideas on which practice is based (6)
27 Swan's chick (6)

DOWN

1 Occur simultaneously (8)
2 Very light wood (5)
3 Body part to pierce (3,4)
5 Diplomatic agent (5)
6 Athlete who leaps over barriers (7)
7 Smell strongly (4)
8 Bristled tooth-cleaner (5)
13 Excellently preserved (4-4)
15 Beat, thrash (7)
17 Lined or creased (7)
18 Garden digging tool (5)
20 Belonging to several people (5)
22 Pretend (5)
23 Rabbit's tail (4)

Puzzle 229

ACROSS

1 Moral principles (6)
4 Suppress (6)
8 Came to an end, became void (6)
10 Fast projectile (6)
11 Orchard's produce (5)
12 Well-behaved (4)
14 Part of the leg (4)
15 Causing (9)
17 Rigid adherent to doctrine (9)
20 (From) a great distance (4)
21 Vessel for conveying tears or bile (4)
22 Shrewd, sharp (5)
24 Grow smaller (6)
25 Fit for consumption (6)
26 Naked lifestyle (6)
27 Covered with heavenly bodies (6)

DOWN

1 Tribute, praise (6)
2 US urban music genre (3,3)
3 Musical symbol (4)
5 Strained (4)
6 Routine office task (6)
7 Whichever of two (6)
9 Percussionist's tool (9)
10 Measure of population growth (5,4)
13 Hot air blower (5)
14 Pummel (dough) (5)
16 Rector, priest (6)
17 Divine (6)
18 Figure (6)
19 Very determined (6)
22 Hard-working insects (4)
23 Revise for the press (4)

Puzzle 230

ACROSS

1 Latitude, range (5)
4 Bedraggled (7)
9 Metric unit of weight (8)
10 Port side of a boat (4)
11 From a lower to a higher position (6)
12 Release from bonds (5)
13 Honest, sincere (4)
15 Breathe one's last (3)
16 Affectionate (4)
17 Hoarse (5)
19 Malfunction (6)
21 Cheque counterfoil (4)
22 Protest (8)
23 Vacuousness (7)
24 Hemmed (5)

DOWN

2 Thin, dry and brittle (5)
3 Process of validating a will (7)
5 Fun activity played at a screen or monitor (8,4)
6 Vacant (property) (5)
7 First score at tennis? (7)
8 Amount by which imports exceed exports (5,7)
14 US phrase meaning 'yes, definitely' (5,2)
16 Ruched (7)
18 Of a city (5)
20 ___ and Punishment, Dostoyevsky novel (5)

Puzzle 231

ACROSS

1 Patella (7)
5 Pottery fragment (5)
8 Chamfered edge (5)
9 Flask (7)
10 Cadence (4)
11 Collie, eg (8)
13 Vicissitudes (3,3,5)
17 Main street (4,4)
19 Japanese wrestling (4)
21 Leave suddenly (4,3)
22 Heave, hurl (5)
23 Stands up (5)
24 Audibility distance (7)

DOWN

1 Grind coarsely (6)
2 Wrap up (7)
3 Young elephant (4)
4 Fierce feud (7,6)
5 Bone structure (8)
6 Having a weapon (5)
7 Blueprint, plan (6)
12 Brave fighters (8)
14 Feed (7)
15 Brief rainfall (6)
16 Fail to recollect (6)
18 High winds (5)
20 Russian ruler (4)

Puzzle 232

ACROSS

1 Authoritative prohibition (4)
4 Actor's backstage assistant (7)
8 Person unsuited to his or her environment or work (6)
9 Closely confined (4-2)
10 Proverbially descriptive of a mule (8)
12 Swirl of water (4)
13 Kicks off (6)
15 Motive power (6)
17 Begging request (4)
19 Handle successfully (5,3)
21 Set fire to (something) (6)
22 Pristine quality (6)
24 Sunday-roast restaurant (7)
25 Money earned (4)

DOWN

2 Biblical letter (7)
3 Lout (3)
4 Same as before (5)
5 Monetary outlay (7)
6 Without a word of a lie (9)
7 Globular (5)
11 Army officer above a colonel (9)
14 Hide (7)
16 Label on a present (4,3)
18 Valid reasoning (5)
20 Response in speech or writing (5)
23 Red, inflamed (3)

Puzzle 233

ACROSS

1 Making pleats (7)
5 Condiment tray (5)
8 Old naval drink (3)
9 Predatory sea-creature (6,3)
10 Calendar's duration (4)
11 Be towed by a speedboat (5-3)
14 Cold, unwelcoming (6)
15 Playing (6)
17 Prepare and stand by (3,5)
18 Coastal ridge of sand (4)
21 Inedible fungus (9)
23 Promise of payment (inits) (3)
24 Very quick (5)
25 Lean and skinny (7)

DOWN

1 Late, overdue (5)
2 Take place (4,5)
3 Irritation (4)
4 Kindly (6)
5 Mildness (8)
6 Manipulate (3)
7 Conversing (7)
12 Decorative paint effect (9)
13 Underscored, highlighted (8)
14 Person who engages in combat (7)
16 Repellent (6)
19 Sincerely (5)
20 Speak unclearly (4)
22 Computer software facility (abbrev.)(3)

Puzzle 234

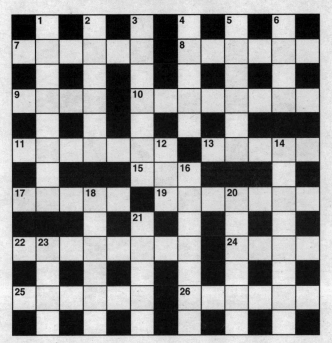

ACROSS

7 Mythical fire-breathing creature (6)
8 Telephone (4,2)
9 Oil and protein-rich bean (4)
10 Empowering (8)
11 Express dissent (7)
13 Sensed with the nose (5)
15 Jump on one foot (3)
17 Proficient, skilled (5)
19 Last beyond (7)
22 Appreciated (8)
24 Unseat (4)
25 Man's ornamental clasp (6)
26 Touch, tinge (6)

DOWN

1 Protected by metal (8)
2 Appalled (6)
3 Free from a restraint (7)
4 Put in the bin (5)
5 Skiing race (6)
6 Move round, whirl (4)
12 In addition (3)
14 Pining for affection (8)
16 Sweet course (7)
18 Reminder (6)
20 View, observe (4,2)
21 Solution of salt and water (5)
23 Eager (4)

Puzzle 235

ACROSS

1 Popular bedding plant (7)
5 Desert plants (5)
8 Grass similar to wheat (3)
9 Effect of heavy snow (9)
10 Fish of the cod family (4)
11 Plan, suggestion (8)
14 Affected imitation of sobbing (6)
15 Within a building (6)
17 Person suffering from loss of memory (8)
18 Be painful (4)
21 People of a borough (9)
23 Make a blunder (3)
24 Sum owing (5)
25 Tiredness (7)

DOWN

1 Stagger (5)
2 Cease to function (5,4)
3 Licentious (4)
4 Bees' home (6)
5 Advancing stealthily (8)
6 Signal for action (3)
7 Narrow-minded (7)
12 Fried, filled, sausage-meat snack (6,3)
13 Look after property in the owners' absence (5-3)
14 Accursed, damnable (7)
16 Yield a profit or result (3,3)
19 Weird (5)
20 Short humorous parody (4)
22 Internet (3)

Puzzle 236

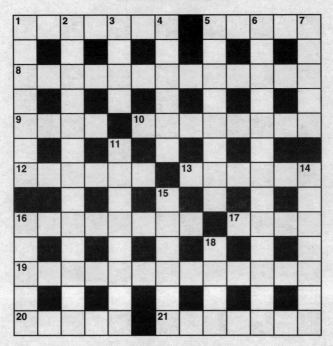

ACROSS

1 Forcing air (into) (7)
5 Cougars (5)
8 Old Mississippi boat (6,7)
9 Cadence (4)
10 Get under way (8)
12 Portly (6)
13 Variety of nut (6)
16 Unlawful killer (8)
17 Eyelid infection (4)
19 Wait impatiently for time to pass (5,3,5)
20 Find disgusting (5)
21 Store that sells playthings (3,4)

DOWN

1 In demand (7)
2 Cope more or less satisfactorily (6,7)
3 In a lazy way (4)
4 Type of industrial action (2-4)
5 Opening statement (8)
6 Make or break, testing time (6,2,5)
7 Sudden swell (5)
11 Forefather (8)
14 Embellish (5,2)
15 ___ poker, spiky plant (3-3)
16 Islam's holiest city (5)
18 Personal pronoun (4)

Puzzle 237

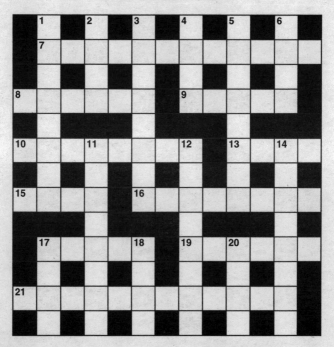

ACROSS

7 Growing of plants (12)
8 Brief look (6)
9 Helpful (5)
10 Reveal, expose (5,3)
13 See red (4)
15 Nibble like a mouse (4)
16 Surround (8)
17 Combine (5)
19 Seat of power (6)
21 Maternal ties (5,7)

DOWN

1 Young people (8)
2 Small British bird (4)
3 Longitude range (4,4)
4 Great degree (4)
5 Represent (5,3)
6 Medical photo (1-3)
11 Fresh blood (3,5)
12 Tight-lipped (8)
14 Gentle nature (8)
17 Act forlornly (4)
18 Orient (4)
20 Bacon skin (4)

Puzzle 238

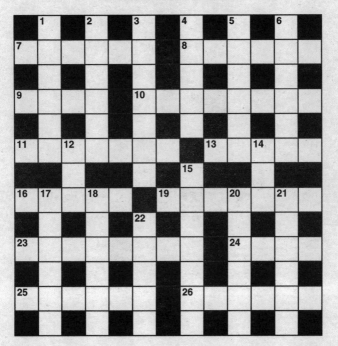

ACROSS

7 Throat passage (6)
8 Roadside stopping place (4-2)
9 Pass over (4)
10 Desist (5,3)
11 Payment slot in a machine (4,3)
13 Recurring series of events (5)
16 Spirit of the lamp (5)
19 Intensify (5,2)
23 Related minutely (8)
24 Brother-in-arms (4)
25 Large flat tracts of land (6)
26 Spheres of action (6)

DOWN

1 Bird whose call sounds like its name (6)
2 Shoe without laces (4-2)
3 Blue cheese (7)
4 Long weapon with a point (5)
5 Warm and cosy (fabric) (6)
6 Intermittent (6)
12 Pub, hotel (3)
14 Fish whose liver produces a healthy oil (3)
15 Timepiece that works by shadow (7)
17 In a uniform way (6)
18 Slanting style of type (6)
20 Very heavy (6)
21 Take cargo from (6)
22 Jaded and offhand (5)

Puzzle 239

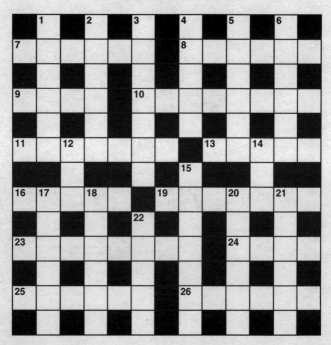

ACROSS

7 Mix thoroughly (4,2)
8 Open out (6)
9 Pass over a barcode reader (4)
10 Break (a law) (8)
11 Time before becoming a man (7)
13 Small pier (5)
16 Underground waste passage (5)
19 Division of the road for PSVs (3,4)
23 Shoveller or scoter, eg (4,4)
24 Cathedral town (4)
25 Expert on a subject (6)
26 Span of eight musical notes (6)

DOWN

1 Fine plaster used for architectural mouldings (6)
2 Credit ___, limit on lending money (6)
3 Fleshy fruit (7)
4 Big curl of hair at the front of the head (5)
5 Reach a place (6)
6 Insubstantial (6)
12 Churchyard tree (3)
14 Infused drink (3)
15 Schoolchild's hamper (4-3)
17 Nostrum for long life (6)
18 Make fond (6)
20 Find the position of (6)
21 Original inhabitant (6)
22 Show the way (5)

Puzzle 240

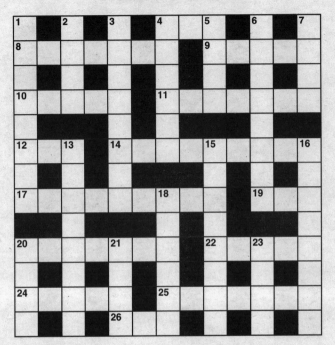

ACROSS

4 Help, relief (3)
8 In the opposite direction to (the tide) (7)
9 Blatant (5)
10 Hair-colouring (5)
11 Underwriter (7)
12 Removable cover at the top of a container (3)
14 ID tag (4,5)
17 Coaxing (9)
19 Family animal (3)
20 Repulse (4,3)
22 Musical play (5)
24 Take exams again (5)
25 Exceptional, distinguished (7)
26 Item of headgear (3)

DOWN

1 Company's ongoing money position (4,4)
2 Flatter in a grovelling way (4)
3 Not merited (8)
4 Glassed-in central courtyard (6)
5 Professors (4)
6 Completely prepared (for) (6,2)
7 Disturbance (4)
13 Person who fights for his honour (8)
15 Loads of cash (3,5)
16 Animal's inner parts (8)
18 Swarm over (6)
20 Firm, unyielding (4)
21 Courtroom promise (4)
23 Bad (4)

Puzzle 241

ACROSS

1 Belittled, depreciated (12)
7 Resolve (4,3)
8 Resident of the Vatican (4)
10 Frenzied desire (5)
11 Potentially eruptive mountain (7)
12 Scoundrel, cur (6)
14 White or cream vegetable often mashed with carrots (6)
17 Hug (7)
19 Of the sun (5)
21 Second Greek letter (4)
22 Signal fires (7)
23 Time when most people take holidays (6,6)

DOWN

1 Produced for as many customers as possible (4-6)
2 Repeat broadcast (5)
3 Cut off from (7)
4 Functioning (6)
5 Force forward (5)
6 Describe (7)
9 Quality of being similar (10)
13 Group of people attractively arranged, as if in a painting (7)
15 Outshine (another act) (7)
16 One of a society (6)
18 Sudden panic (5)
20 Large African cats (5)

Puzzle 242

ACROSS

- **1** Local rule (5)
- **4** Cut out (7)
- **8** (Of a bird) travel to another part of the world (7)
- **9** Show a response (5)
- **10** Afflict (3)
- **11** Agricultural worker (3-6)
- **13** Prevent (6)
- **15** Fine French brandy (6)
- **18** Happy with the world (9)
- **20** Small cask (3)
- **21** Forbidden (activity) (5)
- **22** Paper-folding art (7)
- **23** Tusked African pig (7)
- **24** Powerful clique (5)

DOWN

- **1** Pompous (9)
- **2** Licit (5)
- **3** Endure, overcome (7)
- **4** Absolve (6)
- **5** Welsh breed of dog (5)
- **6** Ease off (7)
- **7** Tiny mark (3)
- **12** Acknowledge (9)
- **14** Small drinking venue (4,3)
- **16** Of long standing (3-4)
- **17** Able to lift heavy weights (6)
- **19** Age (5)
- **20** Battledress colour (5)
- **21** Drag behind (3)

Puzzle 243

ACROSS

1 Enter data (3,2)
4 Come back to (7)
8 Fazed (7)
9 Ill-fitting (5)
10 Bow in the middle (3)
11 Fuel-carrying ship (3,6)
13 Proportion accepting an offer (6)
15 Pungent-tasting plant (6)
18 Levelled (9)
20 Measure of current (3)
21 Musical note worth two crotchets (5)
22 Slant (7)
23 220 yards (7)
24 Person of exceptional holiness and goodness (5)

DOWN

1 Child's play! (4,5)
2 Still in the early part of life (5)
3 Chain of operations (7)
4 Enigma (6)
5 Roman mansion (5)
6 Diver's air tube (7)
7 Foot digit (3)
12 Consignee (9)
14 Teacher or shoe? (7)
16 Obsessive enthusiasts (7)
17 Finishing (6)
19 Rhythm (5)
20 Defence to a criminal charge (5)
21 Heavier alternative to plywood (inits) (3)

Puzzle 244

ACROSS

1 Ancient public clerk (6)
4 To-do, palaver (4)
9 S American dance (5)
10 Car flank away from the kerb (3,4)
11 Cry uncontrollably (3)
12 Lovers' meeting (5)
14 Anti-tank weapon (7)
15 Touch the feelings of (6)
18 Chief journalist (6)
21 One who hires out sailing craft (7)
22 Piece of wood used as a doorstop (5)
25 Female rabbit or hare (3)
26 Warehousing (7)
27 S American pack animal (5)
28 Boorish (4)
29 Way of viewing (6)

DOWN

1 Small species of herring (5)
2 Card game (5)
3 Brag, crow (5)
5 Calm, collected (7)
6 Prolong (4,3)
7 ___ Charlton, footballing great (5)
8 Put right, fix (6)
13 Bishop's office (3)
15 Lie in wait for (6)
16 Relish (7)
17 Authority (7)
19 Frozen hazard (3)
20 A-Z list (5)
22 Sources of water (5)
23 Male duck (5)
24 Worship (5)

Puzzle 245

ACROSS

1 Title-holder (8)
5 Constrain (4)
9 Archetypal (7)
10 Fall from faith (5)
11 Spicy fragrance (5)
13 Driven (7)
14 Filled or covered with a soft material (6)
15 Holder for a sword (6)
18 Change direction (7)
20 Newspapers, collectively (5)
22 Pointed part of a fork (5)
23 Put-you-up (4,3)
25 Measurement of minutes, hours etc (4)
26 Comparable thing (8)

DOWN

1 Chocolate drink (5)
2 Computer language (3)
3 Journey by water (7)
4 Invade (someone else's territory) (6)
6 Capitals (5,4)
7 Distance from one side to the other (7)
8 Scratch (at) (4)
12 Requisition note (5,4)
14 Low wall along a bridge (7)
16 Aspirant (7)
17 Human being (6)
19 Desire (4)
21 Creep crabwise (5)
24 Marshy area (3)

Puzzle 246

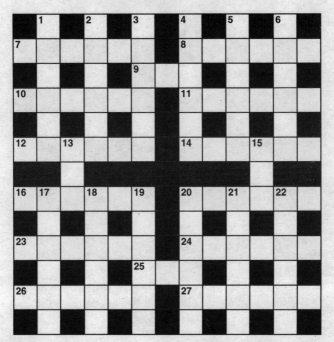

ACROSS

7 Paper size (6)
8 Total assets of a company (6)
9 Hump, haul (3)
10 Instant (6)
11 Yearly periodical (6)
12 Milk container (6)
14 Become bigger or wider (of the pupils) (6)
16 Teased (6)
20 Melange (6)
23 Pertaining to race (6)
24 Person who is new to a field or activity (6)
25 Atom or molecule with an electric charge (3)
26 Have as a consequence (6)
27 Fail to include (6)

DOWN

1 Domelike structure surmounting a roof (6)
2 Enthusiastic (6)
3 Reduced to liquid form by heating (6)
4 Esteem (6)
5 Dig an underground passage (6)
6 Narrow channel of water (6)
13 Commit theft (3)
15 Everyone (3)
17 Chant (6)
18 Alternative name for a refuse sack (3,3)
19 Teachable (6)
20 Having a crew on board (spacecraft) (6)
21 Apparatus, gadget (6)
22 Break out of jail (6)

Puzzle 247

ACROSS
1 ___ up, electrically connected (5)
4 Promoter, financial backer (7)
8 Chicken intended for the oven (7)
9 Loop in a rope (5)
10 Devour (3)
11 Broadsheet or tabloid, eg (9)
13 Computer network trespasser (6)
15 Slow clinching dance (6)
18 Hidden (9)
20 Lady's undergarment (3)
21 Plant life of a region (5)
22 Centre of an atom (7)
23 Elasticated leg-bands (7)
24 Extended part of a collar (5)

DOWN
1 Idea that toil is virtuous (4,5)
2 Of chemicals, undergo change after contact with another substance (5)
3 Easing of hostility between nations (7)
4 Astute (6)
5 Confess (3,2)
6 Autumn birth sign (7)
7 Be sorry for (3)
12 Trial performance (9)
14 Profile (7)
16 Pertaining to the treatment of illness (7)
17 Identical reproductions (6)
19 Escape from (5)
20 Short high-pitched noise (5)
21 Heavy mist (3)

Puzzle 248

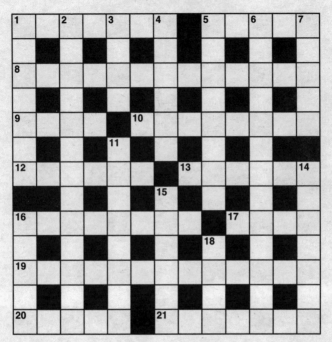

ACROSS

1 Colour very similar to cerise (7)
5 Young women (5)
8 Ceremonial retinue (5,2,6)
9 US TV award (4)
10 Extra player in a competition (4,4)
12 Hand over to the authorities (4,2)
13 Roam aimlessly (6)
16 Yet again (4,4)
17 Lacklustre (4)
19 Item of office equipment (6,7)
20 Sacred water lily (5)
21 Tell me if you've got enough! (3,4)

DOWN

1 Something imaginary (7)
2 Jewellery item with hanging trinkets (5,8)
3 Border (4)
4 Well-informed (2,4)
5 Bargain (4,4)
6 Thorough, radical (4,3,6)
7 Cut to ribbons (5)
11 Hard valuable stones (8)
14 Harp on about something (3,2,2)
15 Small springtime flower (6)
16 Tripe, chitterlings etc (5)
18 Competently (4)

Puzzle 249

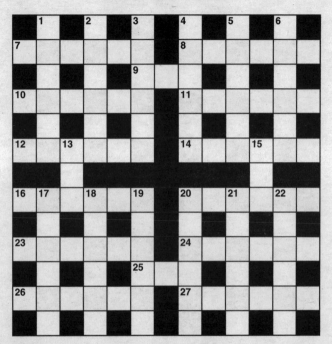

ACROSS

7 Coloured light in the night sky (6)
8 Incidents, occasions (6)
9 Sailing tackle (3)
10 Political shelter (6)
11 Accessories (6)
12 Smile in a silly and annoying way (6)
14 Cross out (6)
16 Prostrate yourself before (6)
20 Officer in charge of finances on a ship (6)
23 Try very hard (6)
24 Go back on one's word (6)
25 Charge for a service (3)
26 Oriental martial art using blows and kicks (4,2)
27 Bound along in a clumsy way (6)

DOWN

1 Cereal, fruit and nut breakfast dish (6)
2 Large blob or portion (6)
3 More friendly (6)
4 Folk tale (6)
5 To do with teeth (6)
6 Ultimately (2,4)
13 Cut (grass) (3)
15 Goddess of the dawn in Greek mythology (3)
17 Choose not to participate (3,3)
18 Items (6)
19 Mournful (6)
20 Simply (6)
21 Cause persistent irritation (6)
22 Christmas drink (3-3)

Puzzle 250

ACROSS

1 Ice-cream container (3)
3 Form of computer entertainment (5,4)
8 Dyestuff (7)
9 Thick dirt (5)
10 Tiny mark (5)
11 Bulging outwards (6)
13 Bob (to royalty) (6)
15 Front of a shop (6)
18 Original, belonging to the earliest time (6)
20 Renounce (5)
22 Subordinate to (5)
23 Rescind (7)
24 Braced (9)
25 Affirmative (3)

DOWN

1 Font (8)
2 Source of irritation (7)
3 Angular front opening of a sweater (1-4)
4 Disconnect (6)
5 Dress fabric (7)
6 Still breathing! (5)
7 Looks at (4)
12 Overshoes for bad weather (8)
14 Old Japanese warrior (7)
16 Guarantee (7)
17 Any non-acid (6)
19 Equestrian (5)
20 Inundation (5)
21 Large deep inlet (4)

Puzzle 251

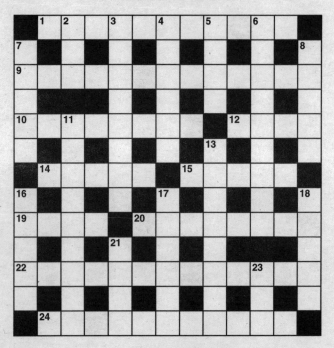

ACROSS

1 Shocking, scandalous (11)
9 Excessively keen to succeed (4-9)
10 Went before (8)
12 Joint in the leg (4)
14 Bad tooth trouble (5)
15 Traffic-light 'ready' colour (5)
19 Chop roughly (4)
20 Shakes (8)
22 Using magic (7,1,5)
24 Murder (a political figure) (11)

DOWN

2 Needle-hole (3)
3 Computer key for inserting a gap (5,3)
4 Pill taken when poorly (6)
5 Ingredient of porridge (4)
6 Decoration (9)
7 Wooden rings (5)
8 SE English county (5)
11 Physical workouts (9)
13 Put in jail (8)
16 What or that (5)
17 Bouts of overindulgence (6)
18 OT hymn (5)
21 *Mona* ___, famous painting (4)
23 Have food (3)

Puzzle 252

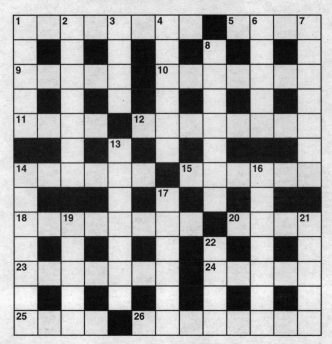

ACROSS

1 Cubic measure (8)
5 Washable floor covering (4)
9 Show a response, behave (5)
10 Directed (people) at a wedding (7)
11 Unruly crowd behaviour (4)
12 Force of personality (8)
14 Basket-weaving material (6)
15 Set of electronic buttons (6)
18 Country's border (8)
20 Piece of sculpture (4)
23 Sparkle in the sunlight (7)
24 Creature from outer space (5)
25 Sicilian volcano (4)
26 Power, might (8)

DOWN

1 Person who looks after another (5)
2 Decider match (4-3)
3 Security camera system (inits)(4)
4 Gave lessons to (6)
6 Cader ___, mountain in Snowdonia (5)
7 One with a lot of experience (3,4)
8 Fizzy powdered confection (7)
13 Speak as someone else writes (7)
14 Political exile (7)
16 Serving (tea) from a pot (7)
17 Salted snack (6)
19 Bulb-like vegetable (5)
21 Next after ninth (5)
22 Own, possess (4)

Puzzle 253

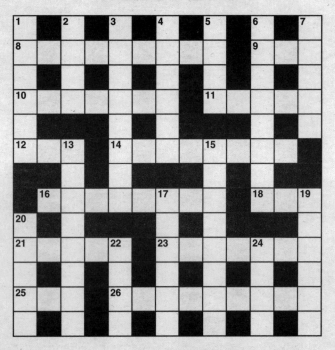

ACROSS

8 Survived longer than (9)
9 Beer (3)
10 Toffee-like sweet (7)
11 Spoon for serving soup (5)
12 Used to be (3)
14 Another time, again (4,4)
16 ___ da Vinci, *Mona Lisa* painter (8)
18 Thing that doesn't work (3)
21 To the time when (5)
23 Man-shaped drinking vessel (4,3)
25 Beach shelter (3)
26 Flower of the Dianthus family (9)

DOWN

1 Russia's capital (6)
2 Mix with a spoon (4)
3 Become less angry (4,4)
4 Style of slanting type (6)
5 Image of a god (4)
6 Rambled, strayed (8)
7 Round flat hat (5)
13 Watch sport (8)
15 Shaft of lunar light (8)
17 Round-trip ticket (6)
19 Discarded cigarette butt (3-3)
20 ___ peas, chip-shop side dish (5)
22 ___ Locket, nursery rhyme character (4)
24 Link up (4)

Puzzle 254

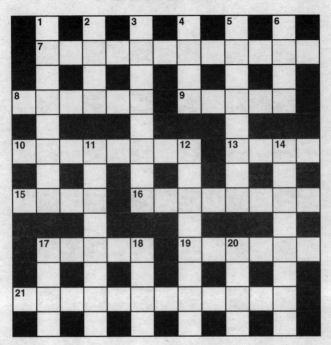

ACROSS

7 Unhesitating quality (12)
8 Incriminated (an innocent person) (6)
9 Driving competition (5)
10 Style of modern art (8)
13 Computer information (4)
15 Half-attached house (4)
16 Be conspicuous (5,3)
17 Dug (for coal) (5)
19 Region around the North Pole (6)
21 Spa town (6,6)

DOWN

1 Lovely, charming (8)
2 Dirty froth or foam (4)
3 Second-hand vehicles (4,4)
4 At any time (4)
5 Comprised (8)
6 Children's 'spotting' game (1-3)
11 Three-sided figure (8)
12 Fruity buns often served toasted (3-5)
14 Sightseeing travellers (8)
17 Mild, submissive (4)
18 Roald ___, author of *The BFG* (4)
20 Looped hunting whip (4)

Puzzle 255

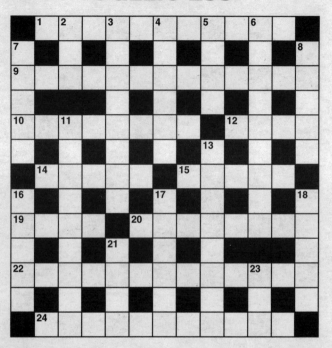

ACROSS

1 Cox's or Royal Gala, eg (6,5)
9 Escorted by, as well as (2,7,4)
10 Implements by compulsion (8)
12 Left, departed (4)
14 Local authority regulation (5)
15 Liquid (5)
19 Parent's sister (4)
20 Five-sided figure (8)
22 Testing a theory (13)
24 Not linked (11)

DOWN

2 As easy as ___, simple (inits)(3)
3 Living for ever (8)
4 Stared angrily (6)
5 Settles an account (4)
6 Hanging around (9)
7 Underwater swimmer (5)
8 Snap taken by a camera (5)
11 Cooking utensil (6,3)
13 ___ relationship, non-sexual love (8)
16 ___ polo, aquatic sport (5)
17 Priest's speech (6)
18 Drawbacks, difficulties (5)
21 Three-piece band (4)
23 Decorate (a cake) (3)

Puzzle 256

ACROSS

1 Walk swaggeringly (5)
4 Ferocious fish (7)
8 Company's bill (7)
9 Waste drain (5)
10 Memory loss (7)
12 Picture, representation (5)
14 Without a thing (5-6)
18 Become putrid (5)
19 Large irregular spot or blot (7)
21 South American woolly pack animal (5)
23 Stops occupying (7)
24 Interrupt (5,2)
25 Stone-worker (5)

DOWN

1 Of the backbone (6)
2 Completely insane (6,3)
3 People born in a pair (5)
4 Pastry-based dish (3)
5 ___ roulette, deadly game (7)
6 This very minute (3)
7 Blow-up mattress (3,3)
11 Burnt remains (5)
13 Yarns, witty stories (9)
15 Between twelve and twenty (7)
16 Small edible bulb (6)
17 Period of study (6)
20 Substitute doctor (5)
22 ___ Baba, children's story character (3)
23 Delivery vehicle (3)

Puzzle 257

ACROSS

1 From the UK (7)
5 Cancer star sign symbol (4)
10 Drink like a dog (3)
11 Buyer (9)
12 Area of very wet land (5)
13 Covers with colour (6)
15 Naked lifestyle (6)
17 Gentle walk (6)
18 Chimney ___, hearth wall (6)
20 On the ocean (2,3)
23 Hair accessory (5,4)
24 Time of life reached (3)
25 Supply nourishment to (4)
26 Safe enclosed area for toddlers (7)

DOWN

2 More mature, more mellow (5)
3 Be a deciding factor (3,3,6)
4 Discarded metal (5)
6 Rice-based dish (7)
7 Tree trunk covering (4)
8 Kettle's heating coil (7)
9 December 25 (9,3)
14 Glad, delighted (7)
16 Hibernating rodents (7)
19 Fish with a large net (5)
21 Nation, country (5)
22 Fifty per cent (4)

Puzzle 258

ACROSS

1 Advance warning (3-3)
4 Film examiner (6)
9 Florida's country (inits)(3)
10 Quality of being circular (9)
11 Arm's sharp bend (5)
12 Intakes of air (7)
14 With nothing to do (2,1,5,3)
17 Purplish-red (7)
18 No ___, road sign (5)
20 Official lists (9)
22 Female undergarment (3)
23 Hurrah! (6)
24 On dry land (6)

DOWN

1 Man's hairpiece (6)
2 Back-up strategy (4,1)
3 Goodbyes (9)
5 Last part (3)
6 Add sugar to (7)
7 Coarse files (5)
8 Speechless, amazed (11)
13 Morning coffee (9)
15 Fastening with rope (5,2)
16 Revolve (6)
17 Shapely and voluptuous (5)
19 Prohibited by social custom (5)
21 Use your eyes (3)

Puzzle 259

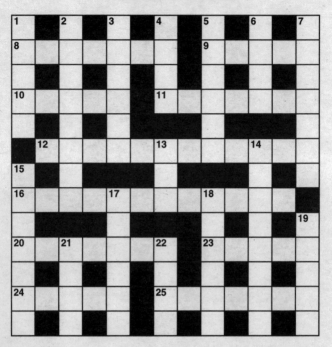

ACROSS

8 Without assistance (7)
9 Humming noise (5)
10 Long hilltop (5)
11 Indian rainy season (7)
12 Make a joint effort (4,8)
16 Taking back from a debtor (12)
20 Dodging work (7)
23 Round white jewel (5)
24 In the immediate area (5)
25 Sparkle with light (7)

DOWN

1 Be quick! (5)
2 Hillside rock fall (8)
3 Word usually ending 'ly' (6)
4 Dutch cheese town (4)
5 Little stab of pain (6)
6 Luxury motor, for short (4)
7 Bread variety (7)
13 Natural source of metals (3)
14 Social gathering of women only (3,5)
15 Cartilage in meat (7)
17 Riot police officer's protective
screen (6)
18 Poisoned, infected (6)
19 Low-ranking office worker (5)
21 Prickly sensation (4)
22 Muzzles, silences (4)

Puzzle 260

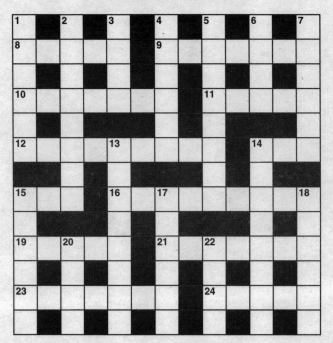

ACROSS

8 Molars, canines etc (5)
9 Electrical joining device (7)
10 Crowned head of state (7)
11 Use bad language (5)
12 Faces up to (9)
14 ___ Fawkes, Gunpowder Plotter (3)
15 Small horse-like animal (3)
16 Bristly quality (9)
19 3rd Greek letter (5)
21 Part-payment in advance (7)
23 Capital city of Cyprus (7)
24 Holder, possessor (5)

DOWN

1 Nuclear (6)
2 Definitions (8)
3 Burn black (4)
4 German town near the Belgian border (6)
5 Daffodil-like flowers (8)
6 Film celebrity (4)
7 Wanting too much (6)
13 Practise (a stage show) (8)
14 Oiling, lubricating (8)
15 White or silver in heraldry (6)
17 Maldives' ocean (6)
18 Sharp humour (6)
20 Small rodents (4)
22 Game like snooker (4)

Puzzle 261

ACROSS

8 Bold, fearless (5)
9 Fridge in a hotel room (7)
10 Available for sale (2,5)
11 One who purchases (5)
12 Fail to make progess (2,7)
14 Sewer rodent (3)
15 Down in the dumps (3)
16 Feeling of pleasure (9)
19 Aunt's husband (5)
21 Get back, recover (7)
23 Herbaceous garden plant (7)
24 Drivers' stopover (5)

DOWN

1 Rectangular (6)
2 Cast away (8)
3 Ridge of coral (4)
4 Appear (6)
5 Condescending attitude (8)
6 Do as you're told (4)
7 Timber disease (3,3)
13 On any occasion (8)
14 Performs again (2-6)
15 Early sailors' illness (6)
17 Country, capital Amman (6)
18 Somersault (6)
20 Restore to health (4)
22 Arrive (4)

Puzzle 262

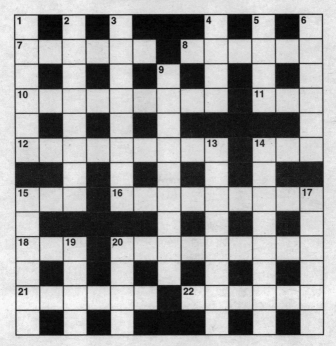

ACROSS

7 Long-term job path (6)
8 Meddle (with) (6)
10 Popular egg dishes (9)
11 Up to now (3)
12 Idlers (9)
14 Cook in hot fat (3)
15 Part of a gearwheel (3)
16 Work overalls (9)
18 Combine numbers (3)
20 Good-luck symbol (9)
21 Mark of disgrace (6)
22 Lamb chop, eg (6)

DOWN

1 Place of learning (6)
2 Producing offspring (8)
3 Umpired (8)
4 Feline creatures (4)
5 Active, nimble (4)
6 Pleasant to look at (6)
9 Large mountain-rescue dog (2,7)
13 Humiliating (8)
14 Non-rented (8)
15 Lacking delicacy, rough (6)
17 Soaked with perspiration (6)
19 Leak slowly (4)
20 Dwelling (4)

Puzzle 263

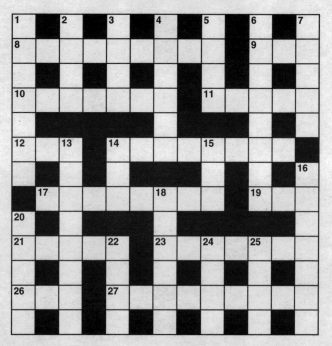

ACROSS

8 Eavesdropped (9)
9 Pasture (3)
10 Spendthrifts, squanderers (7)
11 Only just warm (5)
12 Chafe (3)
14 Trachea (8)
17 Lacking knowledge (8)
19 Cereal grass (3)
21 String or rope (5)
23 Shakes like a jelly (7)
26 Had a meal (3)
27 UK postal service (5,4)

DOWN

1 Dispatch, send on (7)
2 Permits (4)
3 Footwear item (4)
4 Dried grape (6)
5 Correct, check (a text) (4)
6 Insect trap (8)
7 Bow-legged (5)
13 Highland musician (8)
14 Which people? (3)
15 Lump (of butter) (3)
16 Stoat-like animals (7)
18 Forever (6)
20 Thin length of leather (5)
22 Continental currency unit (4)
24 Having no hair (4)
25 Be at an angle (4)

Puzzle 264

ACROSS

1 Capital of the Bahamas (6)
5 Rider's seat (6)
8 Sport played on horseback (4)
9 Devote, pledge (8)
10 Grazing lands (8)
11 Expected standard (4)
12 Space vehicle (6)
14 Setting (a table) (6)
16 Eye swelling (4)
18 Christmas play (8)
20 Scribbles on walls (8)
21 ___ and proper, stiffly formal (4)
22 Soldier's ID disc (3,3)
23 Vehicle repair building (6)

DOWN

2 Guacamole ingredient (7)
3 Talent seeker (5)
4 Comprehension (13)
5 Extremely amusing (4-9)
6 Proper behaviour (7)
7 Sometime in the future (5)
13 Stay in trim (4,3)
15 Zilch (7)
17 Trunk of a statue or body (5)
19 Snake (5)

Puzzle 265

ACROSS

1 More powerful (8)
6 Silly (4)
8 Additional part of a building (6)
9 Young lover of an older woman (3,3)
10 Goes downwards (8)
13 Sleeveless coat (4)
14 Bomb's trigger (9)
17 Noise of shutting a door hard (4)
18 Aristocracy (8)
19 London river (6)
21 Have ambitions (6)
23 Extend across (4)
24 Imperilled, at risk (2,6)

DOWN

2 Christmas decoration (6)
3 Single number (3)
4 Learner, rookie (9)
5 Decay (3)
6 College for non-boarders (3,6)
7 Drooping, sagging (6)
11 Chaplain, priest (9)
12 Ship's right-hand side (9)
15 Do the dishes (4,2)
16 Die from hunger (6)
20 Runner for snow travel (3)
22 Pig's enclosure (3)

Puzzle 266

ACROSS

1 ___ on, encourage (4)
4 Gorges oneself (8)
8 Telltale (6)
9 Bonkers, senseless (6)
10 Sweet and pretty (baby) (4)
11 Votes in a second time (2-6)
13 Involving several countries (13)
16 Small rocky body orbiting the Sun (8)
19 Undergarment (4)
20 Youth ___, lodging house (6)
22 Mauve, purple (6)
23 Jailed (2,6)
24 Average (2-2)

DOWN

2 Swinging weights (9)
3 Tactical withdrawal (7)
4 Different, alternative (5)
5 Important, respected (7)
6 Follow as a result (5)
7 Number of years in a decade (3)
12 Moves between football clubs (9)
14 Strings of pasta (7)
15 Easily seen and understood (7)
17 Come in (5)
18 County next to Cornwall (5)
21 ___ up, admit (3)

Puzzle 267

ACROSS

1 Daily grind (3,4)
5 Quaint, cute (4)
10 Aural discomfort (7)
11 Weapon with a blade (5)
12 Grass colour (5)
13 Hot ___, controversial topic (6)
15 Had a quarrel (6)
17 Medical centre (6)
19 Admirer, wooer (6)
20 Malicious fire-starting (5)
23 ___ candle, firework (5)
24 Dried fruit (7)
25 Loathe, detest (4)
26 Unfastening (7)

DOWN

2 Share the same view (5)
3 Joining up again (12)
4 Weird, spooky (6)
6 Expressed on paper (7)
7 Divisible by two (4)
8 Brussels resident (7)
9 Ninepins lane (7,5)
14 Public disgrace (7)
16 Food connoisseur (7)
18 Place of custody (6)
21 Wood treatment (5)
22 Curved part of a building (4)

Puzzle 268

ACROSS

1 Spot, observe (6)
4 Fastener for papers (6)
9 Outskirts of a city (7)
10 To do with the organ of smell (5)
11 Dishonest scheme (4)
12 Inquisitive (7)
14 Right on time (6)
16 Able to resist infection (6)
19 Clear quartz (7)
21 ___ out, distribute (4)
23 Dust balls (5)
24 Brief outline (7)
25 Dear, expensive (6)
26 For men and women (6)

DOWN

1 Bird's home in a tree (4)
2 Leaves for smoking (7)
3 IT data storage accessory (2-3)
5 Temper fit (7)
6 Italian sauce (5)
7 Became a soldier (8)
8 UK pet charity (inits)(5)
13 Less general (8)
15 Pathetic, wretched (7)
17 Drops off cargo (7)
18 Group of pupils (5)
20 Opposite of 'mine' (5)
21 Evil fiend (5)
22 North American wild cat (4)

Puzzle 269

ACROSS

1 Go forward (7)
5 Smart ___, know-all (4)
10 Popular large house plant (5)
11 Deadly poison (7)
12 Performer, entertainer (7)
14 Greek letter or small amount (4)
16 Rubbishy (6)
18 Publicly reveal (6)
20 Final word of a prayer (4)
21 Base structure of a vehicle (7)
24 Spoke, voiced (7)
25 Place to dance to recorded pop music (5)
27 Agreement, treaty (4)
28 Money management (7)

DOWN

2 Medic, in short (abbrev)(3)
3 Accumulate (5)
4 Ran after, followed (6)
6 Extends (9)
7 Male bird (4)
8 Dictators (7)
9 Allocate (6)
13 Very distressing (9)
15 Scotland's largest city (7)
17 Craving food (6)
19 Sharp-tasting (6)
22 Attached item (3-2)
23 Tyre inflating device (4)
26 ___ up, recap (3)

Puzzle 270

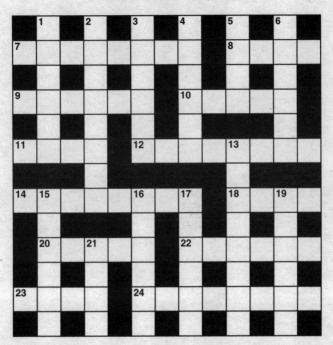

ACROSS

7 Fence preservative (8)
8 Every one (4)
9 Spiced sausage (6)
10 Additional, surplus (5)
11 Iranian branch of orthodox Islam (4)
12 Garden pest (8)
14 Sports shoe with a blade (3,5)
18 Small truncheon (4)
20 Windscreen's cleaner (5)
22 Assemble, form a group (6)
23 Car's warning device (4)
24 Orange pieces (8)

DOWN

1 Violation (of the peace) (6)
2 At the present time (8)
3 Dull, tedious (6)
4 Erase (6)
5 Shed tears (4)
6 Write untidily (6)
13 Suit accessories (8)
15 Cattle herder in a western (6)
16 From one side to the other (6)
17 Hold (someone's attention) (6)
19 Spanish afternoon snooze (6)
21 Pastel shade (4)

Puzzle 271

ACROSS

7 Silhouettes, profiles (8)
8 Egg on (4)
9 Country, capital Ottawa (6)
10 In no particular order (6)
11 Amending (7)
13 Speak off the cuff (2-3)
15 Unfit, bungling (5)
17 Send, dispatch (7)
19 Pertaining to race (6)
21 Scary type of film (6)
23 Carpet-like plant (4)
24 Theatre doctors (8)

DOWN

1 Fish, often canned (4)
2 Bendable (6)
3 Spooky, weird (7)
4 One who consumes or operates (4)
5 Totally spoilt (6)
6 Paying no attention to (8)
12 Charitable offering (8)
14 Not in any place (7)
16 Discipline, chastise (6)
18 Water-ice dessert (6)
20 Wooden barrel (4)
22 Pig noise (4)

Puzzle 272

ACROSS

- **1** Film theatre (6)
- **4** Conan Doyle's detective (6)
- **8** Breakfast food (5)
- **9** Daunt, intimidate (7)
- **10** Stylish, graceful (7)
- **11** Female character in *The Lord of the Rings* (5)
- **12** Assist in eating (5-4)
- **17** Military brass instrument (5)
- **19** In an aircraft or ship (2,5)
- **21** Roman vehicle (7)
- **22** Field of sporting contests (5)
- **23** Stockholm's country (6)
- **24** Dispatched in the mail (6)

DOWN

- **1** Spider's snare (6)
- **2** Centre of an atom (7)
- **3** Craze, obsession (5)
- **5** Perform surgery (7)
- **6** Cat's sound (5)
- **7** Brownish-yellow pigment (6)
- **9** Electing to be excluded (6,3)
- **13** Former, previous (3-4)
- **14** Regional speech (7)
- **15** Bead counting frame (6)
- **16** Queen's youngest son (6)
- **18** Level or rank (5)
- **20** Audience's cry of approval (5)

Puzzle 273

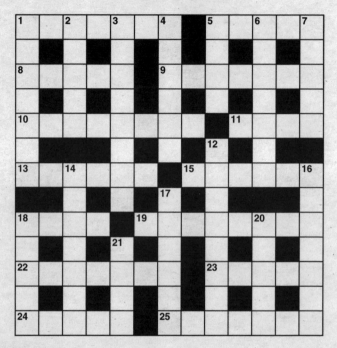

ACROSS

1 Crying (2,5)
5 Fundamental (5)
8 Spicy Mexican dip (5)
9 Month after September (7)
10 Prepared yourself (3,5)
11 Affectionate peck (4)
13 Castle tower (6)
15 Difficult experience (6)
18 Cut (hair) (4)
19 Cooking container (8)
22 Ruled as a monarch (7)
23 Extreme fear (5)
24 Finger or toe (5)
25 Working surface of a table (7)

DOWN

1 Deep understanding (7)
2 Available for renting (2,3)
3 Roused from sleep (8)
4 Of inferior quality (6)
5 The two together (4)
6 Sink down (7)
7 Ringlets (5)
12 Goes before (8)
14 Spoiling, wrecking (7)
16 Stood in rows (5,2)
17 Swiftly attacked (6)
18 Weary, sleepy (5)
20 Kilt fold (5)
21 Midge (4)

Puzzle 274

ACROSS

7 Validates (8)
8 Design on metal (4)
9 Take cargo from (6)
10 Give permission (6)
11 Ever so many (7)
13 Poisonous (5)
15 Diving aid (5)
17 Glens (7)
19 Official population count (6)
21 Needing companionship (6)
23 Aquatic mammal (4)
24 Wilt, lose vitality (8)

DOWN

1 Official robe (4)
2 Strenuous exertion (6)
3 Plods (7)
4 China's continent (4)
5 Releases his or her grip (4,2)
6 Revealingly (dressed) (8)
12 Oily striped food fish (8)
14 Brave or chivalrous (7)
16 Excited activity (6)
18 Join forces (4,2)
20 Exchange of items for money (4)
22 Speech impediment (4)

Puzzle 275

ACROSS

1 Largest bird (7)
5 Sit-down wash (4)
8 Cocktail fruit (5)
9 Flat pasta sheets (7)
11 Isle of Napoleon's exile (4)
12 Make very upset (8)
15 Put money by (5)
16 Book-length story (5)
19 In progress (5,3)
21 Part of a staircase (4)
23 Be ahead of (7)
25 Hangman's loop (5)
26 How soon? (4)
27 Noble lady (7)

DOWN

2 Windsurfing craft (9)
3 Spool (4)
4 Lassie-type dog (6)
5 Constricting snake (3)
6 Gripping utensil (5)
7 Slept lightly (5)
10 Amusing TV show (6)
13 Voting occasions (9)
14 University award (6)
17 Rich cake (6)
18 Shopping trip (5)
20 Magnetic direction (5)
22 Measure of length (4)
24 Deceive, swindle (3)

Puzzle 276

ACROSS

1 Keep secret (4,2)
4 Closed up tightly (6)
8 Fractured (7)
10 Liquefied (5)
11 Kettle vapour (5)
12 Neck band (6)
13 Riches, abundance (6)
15 Unique occurrence (3-3)
19 Artist's workroom (6)
21 Persuade, entice (5)
24 Number-calling game (5)
25 Defeat decisively (7)
26 Cups, saucers etc (3,3)
27 Dessert, colloquially (6)

DOWN

1 Tool for cutting metal (7)
2 Extra, left over (5)
3 Not well groomed (7)
5 Join a course (5)
6 Many years back (4,3)
7 Time units (4)
9 Pond bird (4)
14 Aerial or feeler (7)
16 Vegetarian bake (3,4)
17 Physical well-being (7)
18 Canoe or kayak, eg (4)
20 Male bee (5)
22 Ground-up beef (5)
23 Aid (a criminal) (4)

Puzzle 277

ACROSS

1 Scottish emblem (7)
5 Betting prices (4)
9 Ugly sight (7)
10 Sound receiver (5)
11 Burglar deterrent (5)
12 Beginning (6)
14 Walking aid (6)
16 Game participant (6)
18 Arctic Inuit (6)
19 Dangerous exploit (5)
22 Cause mirth (5)
23 Orator's platform (7)
24 Titled woman (4)
25 Intense blaze (7)

DOWN

2 'Laughing' animal (5)
3 Vending device (4,7)
4 Hide away (3,3)
6 Unsteady on your feet (7)
7 Spill over, splash (4)
8 Repeat contest (7)
10 Noisy viper (11)
13 False reason, excuse (7)
15 Weak, frail (7)
17 Make less tight (6)
20 Belonging to a city (5)
21 Rain turned to ice (4)

Puzzle 278

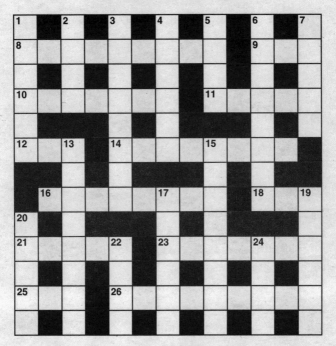

ACROSS

8 Musical group (5,4)
9 Rotten, bad (3)
10 Imprecise (7)
11 Fruit with a core (5)
12 Seeing organ (3)
14 Sieved (8)
16 Silver medallist (6-2)
18 Cutting tool (3)
21 Royal domain or kingdom (5)
23 Under a false impression (7)
25 Highest or lowest playing-card (3)
26 Person applying a wall finish (9)

DOWN

1 Do a favour (6)
2 Wickerwork material (4)
3 Hired killer (8)
4 Quicker (6)
5 Notion, thought (4)
6 Flatten to make smaller (8)
7 Bid (5)
13 Having been taught (8)
15 Rude, bad-mannered (8)
17 Try to get through on the phone again (6)
19 Tall boots (6)
20 Sound of pain or anguish (5)
22 Wear a long face (4)
24 Mend (socks) (4)

Puzzle 279

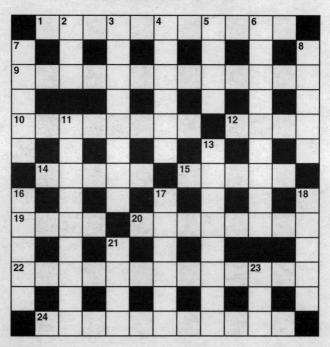

ACROSS

1 Popular buffet item (7,4)
9 Classic fairy tale opening (4,4,1,4)
10 Set off on a voyage (8)
12 Famous loch (4)
14 Merry, cheerful (5)
15 End of life (5)
19 ___ John Silver, pirate (4)
20 Physical (punishment) (8)
22 Relax after being tense (7,6)
24 Development (11)

DOWN

2 Curving line (3)
3 Directly (8)
4 Food shopkeeper (6)
5 Care for, bring up (4)
6 Red ___, English cheese (9)
7 Drilled (a hole) (5)
8 Noisy web-footed birds (5)
11 Large grizzly animal (5,4)
13 Spotted animals (8)
16 Orb, sphere (5)
17 Cartoon sailor (6)
18 Assassinates (5)
21 Antlered male deer (4)
23 Self-importance (3)

Puzzle 280

ACROSS

1 Inn landlord (8)
5 Take notice (4)
9 Long firearm (5)
10 Circus tumbler (7)
11 Saturate (4)
12 First-rate (3-5)
14 Exactly right (4,2)
15 Human being (6)
18 Lovely specimens (8)
20 Scottish lake (4)
23 Worship, adore (7)
24 Disney deer film (5)
25 Twelve-month period (4)
26 Filbert, cob (8)

DOWN

1 Capital city of France (5)
2 Large horned wild ox (7)
3 Decorated (a cake) (4)
4 South American river (6)
6 Monastery head (5)
7 Room for cooking (7)
8 Pepper mill (7)
13 Include, hold (7)
14 Monetary aid (7)
16 Entertainers (7)
17 St ___, Atlantic island (6)
19 Pleasant smell (5)
21 Lift, raise (5)
22 Competent (4)

Puzzle 281

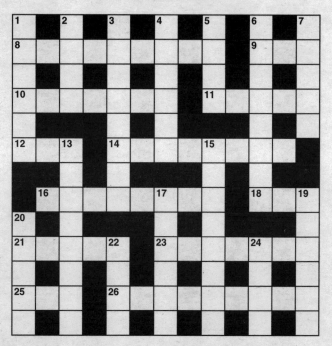

ACROSS

8 Animated quarrel (4-5)
9 Large tea dispenser (3)
10 Difference in opinion (7)
11 Courage, coolness (5)
12 Score of zero (3)
14 Setting alight (8)
16 Spruces up (8)
18 Weep loudly (3)
21 Cancel (5)
23 London football club (7)
25 Mum's husband (3)
26 Removed by plane (9)

DOWN

1 Make unhappy (6)
2 Food in shells (4)
3 Protester (8)
4 Author (6)
5 Religious song (4)
6 Airstreams (8)
7 Heavenly messenger (5)
13 Clear fizzy drink (8)
15 Mass panic (8)
17 Chaperone (6)
19 Cognac (6)
20 Rugged, durable (5)
22 Bakery product (4)
24 Plot, location (4)

Puzzle 282

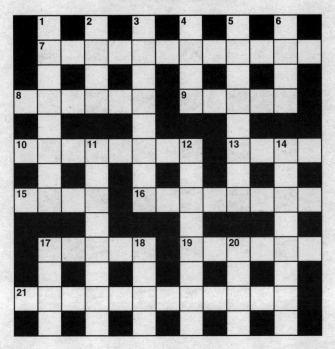

ACROSS

7 Avoid (5,5,2)
8 Capital of Germany (6)
9 Commenced (5)
10 Freaky specimens (8)
13 Back of the neck (4)
15 Rim, border (4)
16 Betting people (8)
17 Backless seat (5)
19 Over-diluted (6)
21 Skittles venue (7,5)

DOWN

1 Rose, went up (8)
2 Hand out cards (4)
3 Permitting (8)
4 Black playing-card (4)
5 Close to the limit (8)
6 Metal money (4)
11 Frozen confection (3,5)
12 To a certain extent (8)
14 Plays the part of (8)
17 End or cease (4)
18 Gave temporarily (4)
20 Notify (4)

Puzzle 283

ACROSS

1 Digital record (7,4)
9 Further check (2-11)
10 Rambling on (8)
12 Old Russian ruler (4)
14 Hard outer part of bread (5)
15 Shipbuilding bolt (5)
19 Kitchen fitment (4)
20 Ride behind a motorboat (5-3)
22 Manage somehow (6,7)
24 Pedestrian tunnels (11)

DOWN

2 Honours system award (inits)(3)
3 Record selection (8)
4 Customer (6)
5 Pull along the ground (4)
6 Unmarried women (9)
7 Becomes larger (5)
8 Nasal sound (5)
11 Not allowed (9)
13 Guns (8)
16 Gin ___, card game (5)
17 Portable computer (6)
18 Brawl (5)
21 Run away (4)
23 Employ for some purpose (3)

Puzzle 284

ACROSS

1 Senior in years (5)
4 Let go of (7)
8 Hit the hay (2,2,3)
9 Bird noise (5)
10 From Istanbul (7)
12 More mature, more mellow (5)
14 Alcohol abstainer (11)
18 Rubbery material (5)
19 Reading stand (7)
21 Gin mixer (5)
23 Dear to the heart (7)
24 Woman's accessory (7)
25 Container for tea (5)

DOWN

1 Half of a quarter (6)
2 Washing powder (9)
3 Jewish religious teacher (5)
4 Colour of rubies (3)
5 Word-for-word (7)
6 (They) exist (3)
7 Demand with menace (6)
11 Travellers' accommodation (5)
13 Pickled (9)
15 Vehicle for hire (7)
16 Grip tightly (6)
17 At some future point (3,3)
20 Baby's tummy-ache (5)
22 Granny (3)
23 Enormous (3)

Puzzle 285

ACROSS

1 Confidential (7)
5 Sigh with pain (4)
10 Not cooked (3)
11 Objects, protests (9)
12 Monte ___, Monaco's city (5)
13 Motto, catchphrase (6)
15 Place where lashes grow (6)
17 Ill-will, spite (6)
18 Moulded, formed (6)
20 Complete, absolute (5)
23 Stated publicly (9)
24 Double-decker (3)
25 Horn's sound (4)
26 Smiled broadly (7)

DOWN

2 Oarsman (5)
3 Red soft fruit (8,4)
4 Occasions (5)
6 Paper-folding art (7)
7 Slang word for 'food' (4)
8 Smashed (7)
9 Unexpectedly (3,2,1,6)
14 Clean out (a refrigerator) (7)
16 Raise in quality (7)
19 Interior design (5)
21 Furniture item (5)
22 Meat from a young sheep (4)

Puzzle 286

ACROSS

1 Oil-yielding seed (6)
4 Stand about idly (6)
9 Flying service (inits)(3)
10 Having no sound (9)
11 Accustoms to solid food (5)
12 Metric farmland unit (7)
14 Restlessly (11)
17 Exaggerated enthusiast (7)
18 Communicate by computer (5)
20 Ocean travellers (9)
22 Metal in an unprocessed state (3)
23 First name of Motown singer Mr Wonder (6)
24 TV commercial (6)

DOWN

1 Canny, astute (6)
2 Bulgaria's capital city (5)
3 Pit entrance (9)
5 Have a debt (3)
6 End of a foot digit (7)
7 ___ Lee, tea, familiarly (5)
8 Shrill (sound) (4-7)
13 Abridged (9)
15 Synthetic (3-4)
16 Einstein's first name (6)
17 Abstains from food (5)
19 Overhead (5)
21 ___ Baba, panto character (3)

Puzzle 287

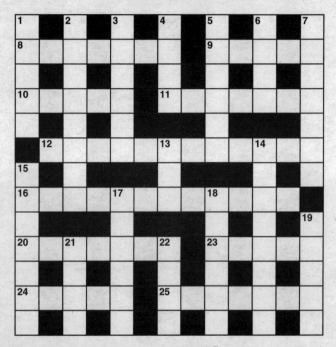

ACROSS

8 Roof of a room (7)
9 Workers' organisation (5)
10 Cooked in a pan, using fat (5)
11 Government trade ban (7)
12 Place for water exercise (8,4)
16 One of the main food groups (12)
20 Consumed with worry (7)
23 Oak tree seed (5)
24 Extended morning snooze (3-2)
25 Amount of film shot (7)

DOWN

1 Futuristic stories (3-2)
2 Conflict within a nation (5,3)
3 Good sense based on experience (6)
4 Frightening giant (4)
5 Boiled minty sweet (6)
6 Seaside jetty (4)
7 Heathen, without religion (7)
13 Extremely cold (3)
14 Voluntary, non-compulsory (8)
15 Confused struggle (7)
17 Pleasure trip (6)
18 Motive (6)
19 Stopped (5)
21 A really long time (4)
22 Shirt's wristband (4)

Puzzle 288

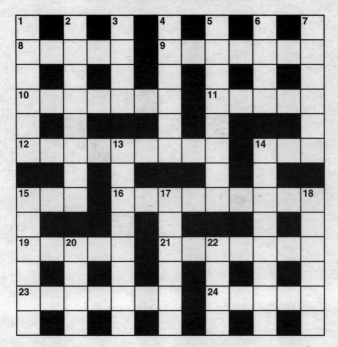

ACROSS

8 Daft, sentimental (5)
9 Leftover item (7)
10 Surgical pincers (7)
11 Short piece of verse (5)
12 British city on the Mersey (9)
14 Human limb (3)
15 Long thin stick (3)
16 Healer of disorders (9)
19 Prickly desert plants (5)
21 Racing car's short break (3,4)
23 Condition of being sick (7)
24 Cool and distant (5)

DOWN

1 Serving a purpose (6)
2 Sanctioned (8)
3 Rubber wheel-covering (4)
4 Hey ___, magician's cry (6)
5 Parasol (8)
6 Newborn child (4)
7 Narrow river (6)
13 Shopkeeper (8)
14 Flying, science of flight (8)
15 Draw back in disgust (6)
17 Place in the open (6)
18 Advance warning (3-3)
20 Phone, ring (4)
22 Bus running on tracks (4)

Puzzle 289

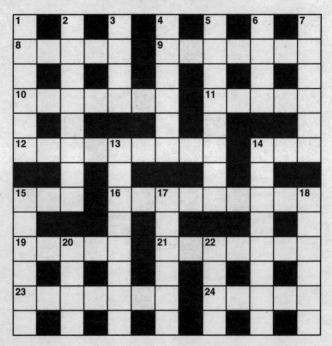

ACROSS

8 Dog's warning (5)
9 Mimic, copy (7)
10 Easy to read (7)
11 Paved garden area (5)
12 Seemed reasonable (4,5)
14 Item at an auction (3)
15 Plant liquid (3)
16 Job interviews for actors (9)
19 Strongly encouraged (5)
21 Police photograph (7)
23 Imaginary mischievous sprite (7)
24 Artificial (5)

DOWN

1 Political refuge (6)
2 Joined in opposition (against) (6,2)
3 Concrete chunk (4)
4 Racing bird (6)
5 Least difficult (8)
6 Wish for (4)
7 Expel from a country (6)
13 Shocking incidents (8)
14 Get-out clause (8)
15 Mark, blot (6)
17 Insist upon having (6)
18 Red ___, breed of dog (6)
20 Colour between black and white (4)
22 Present or donation (4)

Puzzle 290

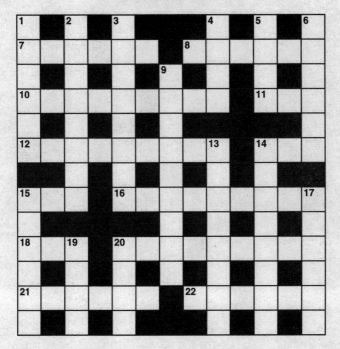

ACROSS

7 Slanted (6)
8 Make (a bomb) safe (6)
10 Self-control and lack of emotion (9)
11 Long-tailed rodent (3)
12 Extremely inexpensive (4,5)
14 (Of a number) not even (3)
15 Voice (your thoughts) (3)
16 Fisherman's oilskin hat (9)
18 Football official (3)
20 Rescued, saved (9)
21 Two-piece swimsuit (6)
22 Toxin, venom (6)

DOWN

1 Looked hard (6)
2 Aerosol insect killer (3-5)
3 Drilling frames (8)
4 Pond lizard-like creature (4)
5 Cat's sound of pleasure (4)
6 Thawed, defrosted (6)
9 Citrus cordial (4,5)
13 Natural hunter (8)
14 Hopeful cheerful person (8)
15 High-intensity flashing beam of light (6)
17 Travelling on a horse (6)
19 Phoney (4)
20 Telephoned (4)

Puzzle 291

ACROSS

8 Puzzle with boxes and clues (9)
9 Have a meal (3)
10 Look after young children (7)
11 Country bumpkin (5)
12 Oil platform (3)
14 Driving too fast (8)
17 Kept hungry (8)
19 Unbuttered (toast) (3)
21 Broadcasting live (2,3)
23 Fail to satisfy, disappoint (3,4)
26 Peg for a golf ball (3)
27 Successful people (9)

DOWN

1 Crisp lettuce (7)
2 Mistake (4)
3 Invites (to a party) (4)
4 Push roughly (in a crowd) (6)
5 Tense, nervous (4)
6 Became feebler (8)
7 Flower stem (5)
13 Weapons manufacturer (8)
14 Look at (3)
15 Useless, worn out (3)
16 Acrobatic athlete (7)
18 Grubby (6)
20 Way of getting there (5)
22 Travel aimlessly (4)
24 Rank, layer (4)
25 Part of a cooker (4)

Puzzle 292

ACROSS

1 Style of sloping writing (6)
5 From Copenhagen, perhaps (6)
8 Active for your age (4)
9 Absolved of sin (8)
10 Overrun by sightseers (8)
11 Cashier's machine (4)
12 African wildlife expedition (6)
14 Life-supporting gas (6)
16 Grew older (4)
18 Bedtime gowns (8)
20 Loan on a house (8)
21 Celebrity actor (4)
22 Come out into the open (6)
23 Two-way sound system (6)

DOWN

2 Starchy milk pudding (7)
3 Egg-producing bird (5)
4 Personal appellation (9,4)
5 Cranefly (5-4-4)
6 Prohibitive road sign (2,5)
7 Aroma (5)
13 One who examines accounts (7)
15 Place in a higher position (7)
17 Man getting married (5)
19 Sense in the mouth (5)

Puzzle 293

ACROSS

1 Infant's glimpsing game (8)
6 Short burst of breath (4)
8 Of a view, attractive (6)
9 Don't lag behind! (4,2)
10 Springtime flowers (8)
13 Plays a role (4)
14 Keen to get on in life (9)
17 Set of two things regarded as a unit (4)
18 Brainboxes, boffins (8)
19 Indulge in idle tittle-tattle (6)
21 Walking, under your own steam (2,4)
23 Jealousy (4)
24 Situated far from the centre (8)

DOWN

2 Audience's cry for more (6)
3 Nearest and dearest (3)
4 Revert to bad habits (9)
5 Ignorant lout (3)
6 Born too soon (9)
7 Out of order, defective (6)
11 Reluctant to be photographed (6,3)
12 Fairground attraction (9)
15 Shallow inland sea (6)
16 Be connected to the side of (6)
20 Go to the next page (inits)(3)
22 Cook in oil (3)

Puzzle 294

ACROSS

1 Wriggly garden creature (4)
4 Hard up (for cash) (8)
8 Association of sports teams (6)
9 Scarily odd (6)
10 Deceitful person (4)
11 Hung around (8)
13 Having an operation (5,3,5)
16 Calming by drugs (8)
19 Square of grass (4)
20 In jeopardy (2,4)
22 Saudi ___, country (6)
23 Meant, had in mind (8)
24 Company trademark (4)

DOWN

2 Act of doing as you are told (9)
3 Stand for holding cups (3,4)
4 Bulge, expand (5)
5 Interval of relief (7)
6 Look into, explore (5)
7 Large deer (3)
12 Carrying out (the law) (9)
14 Cheated, swindled (7)
15 Women's team game (7)
17 ___ in Wonderland, Lewis Carroll character (5)
18 Watch over, protect from harm (5)
21 Heavy weight (3)

Puzzle 295

ACROSS

1 Device for grilling bread (7)
5 Exploited (4)
10 Straighten out (7)
11 Cheese and ___, crisp flavour (5)
12 Canada's leaf emblem (5)
13 Hard area of skin (6)
15 Another name for zero (6)
17 Unbleached cotton cloth (6)
19 Hair-roller (6)
20 Warm and damp (weather) (5)
23 Fracas (5)
24 Predict (7)
25 Lock openers (4)
26 Wart on the foot (7)

DOWN

2 Readily available (2,3)
3 Ghostly tale (5-7)
4 Tempt, lure (6)
6 Incentives or impulses (7)
7 Dip (a biscuit) in a cuppa (4)
8 Call to appear in court (7)
9 Absent-minded person (4-8)
1w More long-winded (7)
16 In the main, by and large (7)
18 Sponge, fruit and cream dessert (6)
21 Melodious sounds (5)
22 Run ___, go berserk (4)

Puzzle 296

ACROSS

1 Put up with (6)
4 Of the whole world (6)
9 Dublin's country (7)
10 Obstruct, clog (5)
11 *The ___ Duckling*, fairy tale (4)
12 Male rower (7)
14 Seize (a criminal) (6)
16 Shoe without laces (4-2)
19 Gangway, aisle (7)
21 Take part in a ballot (4)
23 Alpaca-like animal (5)
24 Drastic, severe (7)
25 Overturn or collapse (6)
26 Took part in a game (6)

DOWN

1 Give out (radiation, eg) (4)
2 Boat for clearing waterways (7)
3 Prepared to start (5)
5 Broad-minded person (7)
6 Be in flower (5)
7 Comparing (to) (8)
8 Set phrase or expression (5)
13 Brochure (8)
15 Coastal barrier (3,4)
17 Earthenware articles (7)
18 High-temperature disease (5)
20 Skin on the head (5)
21 Very necessary (5)
22 Care for, look after (4)

Puzzle 297

ACROSS

1 Gained freedom (7)
5 Dull, uninteresting (4)
10 Narcotic from the poppy (5)
11 West Indian song (7)
12 Jabbed with the finger (7)
14 Heroic story (4)
16 Horrible smell (6)
18 Sewing or knitting loop (6)
20 Cast an eye over (4)
21 Substance left (after processing) (7)
24 Study of the environment (7)
25 Defence of being elsewhere (5)
27 High and low sea movement (4)
28 Marched, hiked (7)

DOWN

2 Glide across snow (3)
3 Having a weapon (5)
4 Put (text) into cipher (6)
6 Published again (9)
7 Period of prosperity (4)
8 Write (music or a story) (7)
9 Most aged (6)
13 Cram people in (9)
15 Stunt-cycling trick (7)
17 Huge gun (6)
19 Private communication with God (6)
22 Heap or pile (5)
23 Toes, heels and ankles (4)
26 Solid water (3)

Puzzle 298

ACROSS

7 Brings to the door (8)
8 ___ and hearty, strong in body (4)
9 Friend made through letter-writing (3,3)
10 Mouth sore (5)
11 Mix with a spoon (4)
12 Mon to Fri! (8)
14 Made numb (8)
18 Smell strongly (4)
20 Adjusted (a piano) (5)
22 Having little width (6)
23 ___ out, scoop water from a boat (4)
24 Taught (8)

DOWN

1 Fraud, trickery (6)
2 Smiled affectedly (8)
3 Bloke (6)
4 Convince or guarantee (6)
5 Elegant, stylish (4)
6 Priests and vicars, generally (6)
13 Photographic processing area (8)
15 Crowd-scene actors (6)
16 Person who doesn't wear clothes (6)
17 Small inflatable rubber boat (6)
19 Ran off to marry (6)
21 Egypt's river (4)

Puzzle 299

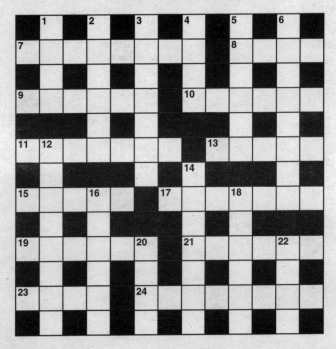

ACROSS

7 Rude retorts (8)
8 Release (a knot) (4)
9 Shrink back in embarrassment (6)
10 Looking-glass (6)
11 Man-made fibre used in knitted goods (7)
13 World-weary sceptic (5)
15 Complete disorder (5)
17 Stiff, formal (7)
19 Estimate the value of (6)
21 Member of the legal profession (6)
23 Official gown (4)
24 Star-like symbol on a keyboard (8)

DOWN

1 With light-coloured hair (4)
2 Too thin (6)
3 Goodbye! (7)
4 ___ bomb, nuclear weapon (4)
5 Slate mine (6)
6 Reprimand, tell off (8)
12 Act of sticking together (8)
14 Gas, electricity or water, eg (7)
16 Unwrapped (a present) (6)
18 Money for finding a criminal (6)
20 Box, fight (4)
22 Opposite of west (4)

Puzzle 300

ACROSS

1 Cosmetics, generally (4-2)
4 Whichever of two (6)
8 Secret ___, spy (5)
9 Small water globule (7)
10 Children's playsuits (7)
11 Leader of a Cub pack (5)
12 Check on someone's finances (5,4)
17 Be outstandingly brilliant (at) (5)
19 Tire out (7)
21 Surveyors, assessors (7)
22 OT hymn (5)
23 Agreement ending war etc (6)
24 Below ___, in the servants' quarters (6)

DOWN

1 Paltry, scanty (6)
2 Say nothing! (4,3)
3 Release from bonds (5)
5 Place in quarantine (7)
6 Divide exactly into two (5)
7 Tradition, ceremony (6)
9 Floods, earthquakes etc (9)
13 Mild illness (7)
14 Frightening tidal wave (7)
15 Soft rich material (6)
16 Cricket equipment (6)
18 Of cows, produce young (5)
20 Go away! (3,2)

SOLUTIONS

Solutions

1

```
B U O     C T A
A W N I N G   C L A W E D
L   C T S   O E   J
S L U S H F U N D   E A U S
A   R E G       U
M I L K S H A K E   C A T
  E   L R   N   A
B U D   Y A C H T C L U B
E     A H C   R
M U G   I N N E R T U B E
O E   N   E O L   W
A T T A C H   I N D U C E
N   S H     E S   R
```

2

```
L A B E L   U N S C R E W
I   L O N   E A   A
B L A S T E D   W H I R R
E   N H O   N N   T
L A D S   E N D   M Y T H
  L A     E H     O
C R Y I N G   P U G D O G
H   T S   M   I
E A T S   A P T   G N A W
E I   T Y   Y E   E E
R U M B A   I M P L O R E
U E   X N   I U   D
P A R T I N G   C A T T Y
```

3

```
C A P O N   H A T E F U L
A   R O A   O O   E
B L O T O U T   P A R K A
L   N N B   S G   V
E D G Y   J O Y   Y O G I
E   B X   H     N
C U D D L Y   T U B I N G
A   T H   T N
R O P E   B U Y   P E E P
P R   S M   A X   I
O P E R A   B I G G A M E
O E   R U   O C   T
L A N D I N G   G E T B Y
```

4

```
  R E J U V E N A T E D
C M   N X   R V   U
R E B E L   P A C K E R S
A A   I E   H N   U
C U R A T O R   E N T E R
K   G T   R     P
  H O O P S   B Y W A Y
P   S A   S S   S
I M P L Y   R O S E H I P
T E   C C   E A   I
H A T C H E T   R E M I T
Y A   I I   U E   E
  B L A C K C O M E D Y
```

5

```
  H I G H E N D   E D G E
S N   E E   M E   L
C A T F L A P   A L B U M
A E   P H   S R   S
M O R A L   E N T A I L
P   E W   E E   P
E X C I S E   P R E F E R
R H   S F   S E
  K E R N E L   W A G E S
S D   E A   I R   E
T I D E S   B E T W E E N
O A   S B   C E   T
P O R E   P Y T H O N S
```

6

```
R E W O R D   W A L L O W
O O   O A   C E   A
C O U P L E D   H E A R T
K L   L O   I S   E
  O D D S   R E E N T E R
Q   B N   V     B
U N E A S Y   D E B A T E
A   P I   B     D
D I A G R A M   F O A M
B R   A A   L N   F
I C I L Y   G O U N D E R
K A   E E   S O   A
E N S U R E   T H I N L Y
```

7

```
G O S S I P   B L I G H T
V   A R   U R   E
V E R Y G O O D   A L A S
R   W O   G T   T
E T C H   F R E N E T I C
  E E       N
  L I N E D R A W I N G
I     M   C
I G N I T I O N   E A S E
H N   N E   P P
S T U N   E C S T A T I C
U E   R I   C L
S P I R I T   A L K A L I
```

306

Solutions

8

```
C U A   B A S
LONELY HUNGRY N
O M F T R E N
SEAURCHIN SAT A
E R E R A A
TAKESHAPE COX
E C S N L
PAD OTHERWISE
R I A M N
OAK DENIGRATE
V A O G I T R
ENLIST ENDING
N E E G C Y
```

9

```
DIARIES CHUG
D L E M L A O
ADLIB ICEOVER
M U G A E Y
POPSTAR NEAR S
I O E T B S
NESTLE COBALT
G T E S S U
IDLE MOUTHED
O A W O L E
GETBACK CABIN
L E Y E E U T
ENDS ADDRESS
```

10

```
A S F P R L
FANCLUB REUSE
F I A A O N A
ESP KINGPRAWN
C E K E M
TIRED MARKING
E E A L E
DICTION PLEAT
E N A O R
LONGSIGHT BEE
O T I E A O A
TALES RESCIND
S Y T H L Y
```

11

```
A S O A T M
ICECUBES HAUL
T A L S E L
BISTRO IDYLL
O H N G E
ANTI GENERATE
N E
BRAGGING SAFE
A M A O A
PLUMB MOURNS
P S I M R O
HERE BOOKCLUB
R S E N E T
```

12

```
P A S E S D
FLOUNCED ATOM
A B U I L C
ENGULF TRICKY
R F V L
SHINGLE SALAD
O E K N N
CLASS INWARDS
D M E G
ABOUND EMERGE
A T A C N I
SCUT STARTOFF
K Y H P S T
```

13

```
G P S B B
ONGOING BONUS
A W O C O R
USED WELLMADE
H E O O
BRANDS DECK
S E A E E K
WOOD RADIAL
L R L P
DOWNPOUR IRON
I E W N U
ESSAY RINGING
T T N S D
```

14

```
ESSENCE FUSE
S L A A I W
CROWS STANDIN
A W Y I P R
ROMP ENTANGLE
E A V G T O
CRUEL SHIFT
C L K Y O A
BEHAVING BREW
A E O S W A
DRASTIC TRACK
L I K I R E
TSAR ASTRIDE
```

307

Solutions

15

```
M A T H S   J I G G L E
H   P   A   E   N E   A
A R R O G A N C E   N E T
P   O   G   C   P E   S
P A N D A   A R T E R Y
Y     R   P       I
  O U T D I S T A N C E
    N     U     B     W
  P A S T E L   A N N I E
C   W   O   A   S   O   A
A G A   W A T C H O V E R
L   R   E   E   E   Y
F E E B L E   O D D L Y
```

16

```
G   S   A   F   S   K   B
R E I M B U R S E   E Y E
U   N   R   I   E   E   R
B I G B A N G   D O P E Y
B   S   H   C   L
Y A P   I N T E G R A L
    E   O     A   L
  S T A N D F O R   M U G
A   E   A   L     A
C U R L Y   C H I R R U P
R   O   O   T   C   O   I
E A U   K N O C K D O W N
S   T   E   R   Y   F   G
```

17

```
C R E E P Y   H U B B U B
A   X   A   T   R   R   Y
C L E A R E R   B L A M E
K   R   S   I   A   I   B
L E T G O   B O N E D R Y
E   N   E     E   E
  G U E S T   S P A D E
A   N   N   E     V
F A L L A C Y   P L A Z A
R   U   O   M   P   R   N
I N C U R   P R E T E N D
C   K   T   H   R   N   A
A N Y W A Y   A S S A I L
```

18

```
  S T U D Y   S H A V E
W   O   I   S   O   I   A
H A R P S   T O W E R E D
O   P   C   I   L   A   D
L I E D O W N   I G L O O
E   D   K   N     O   N
  M O U S E   A G R E E
S   L   T     N   B
K H A K I   H O W E V E R
A   N   P   I   A   I   O
T E N T P E G   F L O C K
E   E   E   H   E   U   E
  E X U D E   B R A S S
```

19

```
R U B B I N G   F O R U M
U   I   S   R   A   E   I
N O T E S   E N L I V E N
U   U   A   S       D
P I C K E T S   I R O N S
    H   E   F   N   E
T R A U M A   T Y P I S T
H   F   A   F       O
U N F I T   L E A R N E D
M     A   A   P     R
B R E E D E R   P A D R E
E   A   O   E   A   N   G
D E T E R   D O L L A R S
```

20

```
M A L I G N   U P W A R D
E   O   A   R   R   R   E
E G O   S U P P O R T E R
K   K   H   O   H   I
L U S T   S T R I P P E D
Y   H   T   P   B   R   E
  A P O L O G I S E
S   R   B   U   T   C   L
C U P B O A R D   S O L O
O   O   G   R   M   O   G
R E C O G N I S E   K E G
C   U   A     R   E   E
H I D I N G   R E N D E R
```

21

```
W A R B L E   S T A P L E
A   A   I   H   W   E   U
R A I N G A U G E   T O R
I   S   H   M   A   N   E
L E E   T H I N K B A C K
Y     E   D     M   A
  T B O N E   S E V E R
A   R   R   X       C
F O O T P R I N T   F O R
R   A   I   S   I   L   A
E N D   T A K I N G O F F
S   L   T   Y   C   R   T
H E Y D A Y   S T E A M Y
```

Solutions

22
```
WASTEFUL   K A
I  P   N BONES
VEIN WIFI E K
E N Q L AKA
SHOT MULLED N
 F S E I C
MUFFIN UNABLE
O F K G U
R HOTTUB SCAN
TEA I N K O
I B NAGS SLAM
FLING F E A
Y T OUTMODED
```

23
```
DOWNCAST CHEW
R I U A W O A
INPUT SWIMMER
E E H Z E N
DOOM WATERSKI
 U N Y N N
COTTON JETLAG
A S F D E
LOCATION BALM
I H R R V E
BRACING CLEAR
R I L E O G C
EARL IDEOLOGY
```

24
```
 J K O U X S
TURNUP SIRENS
 S E T A A E
STEW ORB YEAR
 L L L K
CYGNET EMBRYO
 I U
WHITEN JINXED
 O A A X
PLUG MUM LETS
 D U E J R
POSTAL ARENAS
 N S Y R S S
```

25
```
K E S   C B A
INDUCT PUTOUT
C G E I R R M
KEYIN DIVIDE
B E O Y E H
OVERRULE AREA
X Y Y E O I
EVER GARDENER
R D A I D
 FRIGID TUBER
A O O E I Y
PIPING DOUBLE
P S Y N S R
```

26
```
SONATA A S A
 B G BECOMING
SOSO J U O I
 I GLEAM GAME
 S C E A
STRAIT NICELY
 L U
WHOLLY BARRED
 O E U N
OMIT SINCE A
 E O M G LUMP
PLAYBALL M E
 Y S N EASILY
```

27
```
 S F A S P A
VIOLIN OCLOCK
 E A T N O Q
CRUSHING THUG
 R H B I
TAXI THOUGHTS
 N E O O
HANGBACK RUBY
 V B G L
WIRE RINSEOUT
 A X E O R
ARMADA SQUIRE
 Y M K S S Y
```

28
```
 B O BIB S S
MOTIVE IMPACT
 O L L G A H
PHASEOUT TOOL
 O L N O O
ROWING PAROLE
 A C O N
FORKED BEAMED
 R E O D N
ODDS FUNCTION
 A I T N E U
PISTOL ENSIGN
 N E YET T H
```

Solutions

29

```
C L U M S Y   F O L D E R
L   P   H   A   N   E   H
E X P R E S S E S   S O Y
V   E   R   T   E   I   T
E R R   B L O W T O R C H
R   E   N       E   M
  T E E T H   S M A S H
A   N   C   U       F
B I G H E A D E D   C A R
D   L   A   R   D A   E
U S A   S H O E L A C E S
C   N   E   M   E T   C
T I D D L Y   E S K I M O
```

30

```
B I F O C A L S     P   I
O   L   E   C A R E D   I
A H O Y   U N D O   O   I
S   O   T   M   U F O
T I D E   D I M M E D   T
    E   A   L   I     C
M O D E R N   A T O M I C
O   G   C   S   A
L   T A U G H T   K N O T
L O O   I   R   A   R
U X   N O O K   O G L E
S W I N G   M   E   A
C   C   R E L E A S E D
```

31

```
I C E C U B E   L E A F Y
  H   A   A   S   A   R
C O U N T R Y C O U S I N
R   O   O   R   Z
B U M P I N T O   O O Z E
  S   E   L   L   Y
    I N T E R L U D E
O   E   N   S   C
S C A R   T A K E C A R E
E   I   N   H   I
M A N O F T H E H O U S E
N   N   Y   E   O   I
A S S E T   U S E L E S S
```

32

```
  S   S   M   U C   B
H I L T O N   S N O O T Y
O   I   U   E   I M   E
W O M E N   D R O O P Y
E   T   I   N   E   S
R E C E I P T S   G R I P
I   O   E   I   E   I
N I N E   G O I N G S O N
G   C   S   I   V   S
  C O M P E L   A P A R T
B   C   E   Y   L C   E
B I T I N G   D I T H E R
C   S   T   D   E   S
```

33

```
  S   S L   P   F   P
I N D I V I D U A L I S M
A   D   O   F   A   A
S P L E E N   F I N E L Y
P   R   S   I   M
P Y L O N   E N T H U S E
  A   K   G   I
B I N D I N G   S P A T E
  N   E   A   S   R
S L E E V E   B U T T I N
A   D   P   Y   E   C
W I L D C A T S T R I K E
  D   Y   D   S   S S
```

34

```
  S H A D E   G O F A R
S   O   E E   U   K   W
C A M P B E D   T I A R A
E   E   T   I   B   L
N U T S   S C O R N F U L
I   R   B   T   E   A
C O U P O N   C A N N E D
  T   A   S K   C   R
C O H E R E N T   T Y R E
O   D   O   F   W   S
C A P R I   W I L L O W S
K   O   N Y   O   R   Y
  S T A G E   P E R K Y
```

35

```
C   E   A P   U Y   S
L O V E B I R D S   O P T
E   E   O   U   G   A
F I N A L   P R A Y I N G
T   T   I E   L   I
  M U S S E L S   E D E N
B   A   H   F   U G
R O L L   G I B L E T S
U   T   M   O   Y   A
S K I J U M P   T E P I D
H   N   M O   S A   A
U R N   M A S S A G I N G
P   S   Y   E M   D E
```

Solutions

36

```
  H T A   P P C
HUSHED   REASON
  R R M O N D
ALTO   INVADERS
  N   R E E I
EPIGRAM   GRAVE
  R   L B   E
BOTOX   HUNKERS
  F N S O   I
COVENTRY   COPS
  U W E A K I
UNSAFE   NEUTER
  D Y L T P S
```

37

```
WELLDISPOSED
S N A N A I E
CADET   TWIDDLE
U U T R N L P
MYSTICAL   DEAF
  E C Y I   R
PORTER   SCATTY
E   D P E R
ALSO   BLACKEYE
S I A E R A V
OVERBID   ENSUE
U G L G A O R
PREDETERMINE
```

38

```
 HOUSEWARMING
U P O A E N A
SHUTOFF   ALARM
U L T F P N E
REEK   CLIPPED
P N F E E   S
ENTIRE   PAELLA
R I F R E B
 BARGAIN   STAB
H D H T T D A
EJECT   FARMOUT
R P E U I W H
ENTANGLEMENT
```

39

```
USAGE   HEALTHY
A E A N O A
PUTTOBED   NAVE
N L U E E E
WAYOUT   MORTAL
  S   I   G
JUSTIFICATION
N   R   E
CANDLE   COARSE
R E S O C P
OMEN   HUNGOVER
E I E S S L
ODDMENT   CYCLE
```

40

```
 EPITOME   SPIT
T I A R R O
HEARSAY   AMONG
I N W F Z R A
ELOPE   LOOFAH
V E Y R T I
EXEMPT   OBTAIN
S L A S L C
 VESSEL   AWFUL
A G I U D I U
GUARD   DEEPEND
O N E G N E
GATE   PERFIDY
```

41

```
STRIPE   BLOCK
A A L F L N E
MANNA   EDUCATE
O G T R E I N
SHELTER   ORAL
A R E YEW Y
 TSAR   EACH
C SEA L R A
HEED   BELLOWS
E L F U K Q S
RAFFLES   ELUDE
U I A E P E S
BANDY   STATES
```

42

```
O A G S   T S
DESIRING   GRIM
I T I I A I I
OVERLAP   SHOUT
U R L E K H
SOON   CRUELTY
 I F W I
 IDYLLIC   AMID
S I M B I E
CIVIC   MELODIC
E E K U O I A
NAIL   UNBOLTED
E L E D Y E
```

311

Solutions

```
  S D P   S G R
OUTSIDE CURIO
V I S A R   A U
EAR CORGI MUG
R R   S B   H
STUFFY ABOARD
I   P E   L S I
MISLAY GEISHA
P   T U   U M
LOB HENCE MOON
I O E   I X I N
FOYER TRAINED
Y   S S   Y M G
```

44

```
PROSE CLOSEUP
H C S U   H N
FIVESTAR EVEN
N P U K L Q
POTTED INFLUX
  I       I A
ABACUS GLADLY
R     U     M
COSMIC PRINCE
I I T   I A A
CLAN INCUBATE
E I O K L E
ADAMANT CYMRU
```

45

```
R G T   D B S
BUTLER EUROPE
S E U L O   E
ISLE STICKLER
I   S   E D
SALAMI SHOP
N S NUN U S
  CLOG EATOUT
T O   E   F
WHENEVER DUFF
R G E   I A E
FORAGE NATURE
B S R G E S
```

46

```
S   C E     Q S
CHILLING JUNK
R D O   I B A Y
UNLIT GALORE
B E H M A T O
LORD HANDDOWN
A   A H   E A
NEWCOMER OWLS
D O U X S O T
FOURTH CARER
O I S   U O D
FENS IMPRISON
F G   E E   G
```

47

```
THIMBLE SWAMP
A A O I A O
GRIN BANKRATE
P N E D   T
POKER LONGBOW
O Q   O O
ENDURE REBUFF
I M E A
HOBNOBS AGENT
C   O S G C
GEAREDUP IRIS
A A Y U N E
GNOME BRIGADE
```

48

```
S H A S S T
STOOPS PULLIN
E R T A O R
SPAR ERR GOES
I R R S
WHIFF LOGBOOK
O I R W A M
STACKUP SCREW
D N S K
BRED WIN SAGE
I O I I E A
UNROLL PLAINS
K R D E T G
```

49

```
EGGNOG WAGS
D U U R A R
RESULTANT ARC
A T L I E P O
WOOL ANARCHIC
S A Y W I O
TICKLE FALCON
R I L B Y U
INTERNET SPOT
N A I A A U S
GOD GIVEBIRTH
E H E E S Y
SLAT RATHER
```

Solutions

50

```
I   A R A   A P A
C O N G A   D I S C U S S
E   T   S O   H R   I
F R I P P E R Y   B I N D
L     B   E T F   E
O S P R E Y   T H E I R
E   O R   E E S
  S N O R T   S M U D G E
L Y Y   S   E   V
A R T Y   F L A T M A T E
Y   A E   O U I R
B U I L T U P   N U D G E
Y L   C E E E D
```

51

```
  T S H     B D
W H A T F O R   T R A I L
  A E   R I E   T
S W I M   S Y M P A T H Y
    M D   A K E
L I V E R O U G H   P R Y
  N D   E I S E
A T E   F U R N I T U R E
  R A   V A A
O U T B U R S T   T A M E
  D O   E I U A
H E A V Y   A V A R I C E
  R E     E E E
```

52

```
S E L E C T E D   C H I P
O   A A L   I A
M A R K S M A N   S T U N
E   V H P F B T
  S A R I   S P I N A C H
F   N E S C E
L O A T H E   C H O K E R
Y   G A T M   S
D R A I N E R   O V A L
R   I D Y N N U
I N N S   L O D G I N G S
V   S   U E U E
E A T S   S T A R T L E D
```

53

```
U P P E R S T O R E Y
  R N C U S   S
H O O V E R   T I P P L E
  F O U C O   X
D E F Y   B U R G U N D Y
  S   S Y S E
I S L E S   G E T B Y
  E Y K L   A
A D H E S I V E   B O U T
X   L T S R C
I M P A R T   S W A T H E
S   S E E V E
  C H A N G E H A N D S
```

54

```
S   T S A O S
T O U G H   B O U N C E R
A   R U R T A E
R U N I N T O   D O L L S
T   T A O D C
I D L Y   A D M O N I S H
N   I S R N E
G A S W O R K S   A G E D
O   T B I A U
V A L U E   D I G I T A L
E   E R N I O I
R E S O L V E   L E T I N
  S Y Y E E G
```

55

```
F   R C C G C
U N A P O L O G E T I C
N   S B S T S
D E C O R U M   A L I B I
  A A O W E G
F A L L   A S S A S S I N
A   C Y I
T E A T O W E L   A N O N
N   I M G E
E G G O N   B U L W A R K
N   L B O O R E
  D E M O N S T R A B L Y
  R X S Y Y S
```

56

```
O   B S A Z C A
F L E E C E D   I N L A W
F   N R U N A E
L O T T O   L O C U S T
I   U T   S P
M O M E N T   B A N I S H
I   A G D C O
T E L L E R   O D D S O N
S   T U I E
  C L O W N S   T O N I C
E   O A U I A A
B L A C K   R E V I V A L
B   F E P E Y L
```

Solutions

57

```
R W L     C S B
A F R A I D   S L O W L Y
N   E   C   S   O   I   E
D I S S E C T E D   M O B
O   T   N   E       Y
M I L K S H A K E   V I E
    E   E   M X   A
L I D   E M B A T T L E D
A       A   E   U   E
Y E N   W A T E R M A I N
O   E   I   H   I   B   O
F I X I N G   J O B L O T
F   T   K     R E   E
```

58

```
D O W E L   K E E P M U M
I   E   A   I   A   A   A
S T A R T U P   C H I C K
C   V   E   P   H   Z   E
O M I T   W E B   V E T O
    N   J R P   P       U
V I G O U R   P U N D I T
A   G   R   B   E
R O M P   C U T   A V I D
N   O   Y   L   R   I   R
I G L O O   I R O N O R E
S   A   G   N   O   U   A
H U R L I N G   F U S E D
```

59

```
P I P E R   H O G W A S H
U   A   A   I   R   E
F I C T I O N   S P O I L
K   N   D   T   M   P
Y E A R   A L E   S A R I
    G   P   E   H       N
F E E B L E   F U M I N G
A   Y   P   G   N
T A C K   B U G   U S E S
E   H   A   G   E   T   U
F E I G N   D A Y L O N G
U   N   T   O   E   R   A
L E A D I N G   S P E A R
```

60

```
S E C O N D G U E S S
S   A   A   E   N   U   P
C A R D S   M I L L E R S
O   A   I   A   D   A
F U C H S I A   D W E L L
F   H   N   E       M
R E U S E   K N O W N
C   P   H   R   L
R I F L E   I M A G E R Y
A   L   A   N   T   A   I
C R O O K E D   L E T I N
K   R   E   E   A   H   G
H A I R D R E S S E R
```

61

```
B A F F L E D   T S A R
S   D   E   K   T   U
P L U M A G E   I D I O T
E   L   T   O   N   R   S
C A T C H   U D D E R S
T   E   T   E   U   C
R E B O R N   D R A P E R
E   L   B   E   G   U
P U T R I D   A P P L E
C   B   A   I   R   L   L
R A B B I   B I T P A R T
A   E   N   L   E   I   Y
B O R E   L E A N I N G
```

62

```
R E F U N D   C R A F T S
O   R   I   M   E   L   P
S H I V E R Y   P R I O R
E   L   C   R   L   R   A
  F L E E   R E E N T R Y
J   E       H   T   T   T
A R D E N T   G E I S H A
M   U   F   E   N
B O U N C E R   V I N E
O   S   L   O   I   D   W
R O U S E   T A D P O L E
E   A   U   H   E   F   A
E N L I S T   B O F F I N
```

63

```
S T A T U E   F A R O F F
I   U   A   A   O   O
N A R C O T I C   W O R N
R   K   D   E   E   W
T A X I   I N T E R V A L
    N   R           R
  T I G H T L I P P E D
W       S   R
S I Z E Z E R O   I D L E
S   A   L   L   N   A
S T I R   F L A T T Y R E
E   L   I   T   E   V
O D D S O N   E N D E A R
```

Solutions

64

```
V   S   A     S T   U
I N C O M E   S H A R K S
E   O   B   C U E       E
W A F E R T H I N   E L F
E   F   O   E         U
R E I N S T A T E   P A L
  N   I   P   D   E
C O G   A D N A U S E A M
A       E   C K       E
N U B   D I S P A R A G E
T   U   I   S   T   B   K
E N C A S E   R E C O I L
R   K   H     D   O   Y
```

65

```
  D I A R I E S   C H A T
D   R   E   F   A   E   E
E X E R T   F O R S A K E
N       R   O   M   D   S
S P R A Y E R   A L S O
E   I       T   D   T   P
L A N D E D   S A L A M I
Y   G   G   C   R   T
  T A N G   O V E R T L Y
C   B   N   F   X       I
R E E L O F F   A C O R N
O   L   G   E   C   W   G
W E L D   W R I T I N G
```

66

```
A   O   K     S   U   F
D E M O N I C   L O N E R
D   E   O   O   A   C   E
I O N   T H E O C C U L T
T   T   X   R       R
I M P L Y   I N S U L I N
V   R   S       E   O
E P I T H E T   E N D O W
  G   A   E   N       A
V I G I L A N C E   C O D
O   I   T   C   R   O
T A S T E   E A G E R L Y
E   H   R     Y   K   S
```

67

```
R   A   M   S   S   L
P I E C R U S T   W A I L
  G   A   R   R   A   M
B O N D E D   O W N U P
U   E   E   L       E
D R U M   R E L O C A T E
  I       A
M O R A L I S E   F O U L
U   N   M   F   N
T H I E F   B L E A R Y
W   N   I   O   I   E
S I G N   R U D E N E S S
T   S   M   Y   E   T
```

68

```
  E   C   E   A   D B
S M O U L D E R   E X A M
I   S   U   M   N   N
S T A T I C   S L I N K Y
    O   A       E   R
H E R M I T S   G R O A N
N       E   A       T
C H I P S   T R U S T E E
A   E       C   O
U N U S E D   H O U R L Y
C   T   O   I   R   E
F E E L   V I V A C I T Y
D   E   E   E   E   S
```

69

```
S   C   S     B   F
U N G O D L Y   V O G U E
O   R   E   S   I   R
B U R N   D U C K L I N G
T   E       O       I
  P R O P E R   W A S H
Q   E   L   E   E   H
F U N D   U N R E A L
E       C       R   H
S U N B A K E D   A B U T
E   A   Y   O   W   R
S U L L Y   L O Y A L T Y
P   D       R   Y   S
```

70

```
  A D D R E S S   G A P E
O   O   E   I   E   H
D O W S E   M A I L B O X
D   N   K   I   N       T
L U R K   E L E V A T O R
Y   I   F   E   E   A
A G A I N   B R A K E
  H   L   A   T   E   A
P I T I L E S S   U S E S
D   E   S   S   T   H
H I G H T E A   W H E R E
O   A   I   A   P   S
S M O G   F L Y P A S T
```

315

Solutions

71

```
. A D M I T . P I M P L Y
G . O . C O N . R . O
L O W S E A S O N . I R K E
O . N . D . T . E . O
V I S I T . E R R O R S .
E . . . . E . N . T
. D E V A S T A T I O N .
. N . . . . A . R . E
P R O M P T . I N D E X
D . O . U . I . P . R . I
I O U . S T O P P R E S S
S . T . I . N . E . A . T
C L E N C H . G R I M E
```

72

```
P . S . B . I . U . S . P
S E P A R A T E S . O N E
Y . A . O . A . E . L . T
C O M I C A L . D U V E T
H . C . I . . . E . Y
E T C . O N C O M I N G
. L . L . . A . C
. H U M I D I T Y . Y E T
E . E . N . O . I
S I L K Y . S E R V I N G
S . E . A . I . E . C . H
A S S . W A S P S N E S T
Y . S . N . T . S . D . S
```

73

```
C R E E P Y . W A S H U P
A . R . I . A . D . E . O
C O U N S E L . L I M I T
K . P . T . I . L . A
L E T G O . G I B B O N S
E . . . L . N . . . C . H
. B R A S H . B A N K S .
P . E . . . P . I . . . W
L E C T U R E . R A D I O
A . R . N . A . L . R . E
G R U E L . K E E P O F F
U . I . S . S . N . U
E S T A T E . A S W E L L
```

74

```
. S C O W L . S P A S M .
A . O . E . A . A . I . M
C A M E L . M A C H E T E
U . M . L . A . K . G . A
T R E S S E S . I D E A L S
E . N . . . S . N . L
. I T C H Y . A G R E E .
A . . . I . S . . . Y . A
B O U N D . H A R N E S S
U . R . E . A . O . S . K
S U B S O I L . B R O K E
E . A . U . L . E . R . W
. G N A S H . A D D E D .
```

75

```
T E R R I E R . G A M M A
O . A . R . I . L . O . N
T E M P O . B E A N B A G
U . . . N . B . Z . . . E
P A R T Y T O . I M P E L
. U . . N . E . E . I
P U R I F Y . A R C T I C
A . A . . . A . A . A
R E L I C . S E C U L A R
C . . . T . S . I . . . U
H O R M O N E . D U K E S
E . U . R . S . E . E . T
D I N K Y . S P R I N G Y
```

76

```
D O C K E T . B E D L A M
I . H . A . N . I . U
V I A . R E P E L L E N T
I . I . L . O . A . I
N O R M . S T A R S I G N
E . L . A . P . G . N . Y
. I N T R O V E R T .
S . F . T . U . D . E . C
O U T D O O R S . I N T O
D . . . R . R . F . S . P
I N C E N T I V E . I M P
U . A . E . . . A . F . E
M A R T Y R . P R A Y E R
```

77

```
C A N D L E . C O S S E T
A . O . E . P . V . T . I
R A I N G A U G E . A I M
T . S . I . T . R . L
O R E . B O O K T O K E N
N . L . N . . . E . . . G
. A C R E S . S M I R K .
A . . . O . B . I . . . G
D A Y R E T U R N . W O O
J . N . A . L . S . H . S
U S E . S P L I T P E A S
S . S . S . E . L . I
T U S S L E . T R I P U P
```

Solutions

78

```
BUTTRESS  S U
A E L RACES
THAT WIFI O E
C C P B RID
HOOK TURBAN C
 S D P I A
DAYOUT ANSWER
E S S G O
S HATBOX NUMB
PEA I R N U
I B NEED IDLY
STING L E E
E T CYLINDER
```

79

```
WINGSPAN SCUT
E E I S C A I
INTER SCALPEL
R B E T R L
DRAY GRAFFITI
 L H T L N
CALLUP SARONG
L R B P R
AUDITION MILE
M A F O G D
BOROUGH CLANG
E E L O M E
RUSK DOWNWIND
```

80

```
 S S B S B A
HUNTER MARKUP
 B O A U E R
FLIP NAG WOOL
 E D L R
STICKY YESMAN
 U O
OFFDAY PEBBLY
 A E R I
SNOW ADO COME
 O A V A I
DUFFEL ENMITY
 T T Y N P S
```

81

```
 I A G S S G
DIVERS SPOOKY
E I A C U C M
ADDON UNREAD
L U R S L H
IMPOLITE PLEA
S E E R E I
EYED FLOUNDER
D L B A N S
 MILLED ANGST
B N U S M O Y
LOGOFF DOWELL
T S F K S E
```

82

```
IGUANA F F U
A U SHILLING
GRAN S C E W
R THICK WEEK
E S L L
STRAIT EMBALM
 U A
SMOKED TANNED
 A E A N
BROW MARKS S
 G A U T ARID
WISTERIA Y G
 N T E RISING
```

83

```
 M F C T S I
QUARTO REWIND
 S E V I A D
ALOEVERA GAIN
 I P L G
UNDO DARKROOM
 S O U E
SHUTDOWN ARCH
 A M C O
TSAR SABOTEUR
 S U D E I P
PLASMA VOODOO
 E T Y Y N N
```

84

```
 M W SAG S S
KIMONO OILRIG
 R R L B A G
PRIMEVAL GUNS
 O W E A
ARDOUR TACKLE
 S O A N
SENDUP GILDED
 T A U A N
CHOP SKIRMISH
 I R T D I U
ECLAIR EXTORT
 S Y YES Y E
```

Solutions

85
```
C L A S S Y   S U M M I T
U   P   T   C N I     A
P A R C E L L E D   S O N
T   O   A O E   T   K
I N N   M O T O R B I K E
E     E   H     M   R
  P R U D E   A C T E D
E O   E   A   C
S E T T L E D U P   P A L
C T   I   I   A R   O
A L I   N O T E B O O K S
P   N   E S   L U   E
E N G I N E   L E N D E R
```

86
```
W A R N I N G S     S   A
E   A       R   R U C H E
L A N K   N O G O   O   R
S   I     W C   U F O
H I N D   B U C K E T   S O
    T   S P E     O
T R O O P S   G R A V E L
O     I   H S O
W   B A C K E R   F L O W
A G A   I A     U   A
R   S   N A V E   S M O G
D O I N G E     E   O
S     C   I N U N I S O N
```

87
```
  S P A S M   R A F F L E
S I   C   A N     A D
M O T H E A T E N   N A G
I   T   P M U M Y
T R A I T   O I L C A N
H     I S     I
  P E R C E P T I B L E
  A   H   M     P
  U S A B L E   P O K E R
I E   A R E N   O
D U O   S H I F T L E S S
E F   I C U E   E
A F F E C T   P S A L M
```

88
```
W   S   E     H C   A
A C T I N G   R U B O U T
S   A D S   M   M   M
T H R E E   C L A M M Y
E   D   O N   U   L
P U R S U I T S   O N T O
I   E   P   S   E N
P O P E   R E A L I S E D
E   L   A V E   O
  L I T T L E   E A T E N
A C T   R P   O E
G O A L I E   L I N G E R
E S   C   N   A S
```

89
```
  W   F   V E   S   A
S H O O T I N G S T I C K
  A   R N O   U   H
F L E E C Y   T U N E I N
  E   L L R     N
D R O O P   L I T U R G Y
  C   P P N
S I C K P A Y   E D I C T
  N   D P E   O
A F F O R D   U N R O L L
  A U O P   W D
I M P R A C T I C A B L E
  Y S K L   Y Y
```

90
```
U S U R P   T B O N E
S   T   A A L   U L
C R A M P E D   E X T R A
R   G   T D A   V
I C E D   P U T T O S E A
M   H E P   I T
P L A C I D   I N V A D E
N   G   F G R   X
G O D C H I L D   O B O E
A   T   U S   O M
R I F L E   K O I C A R P
B   I E   L R T
A G O N Y   W O O D S
```

91
```
C   A I S W   S G
L A S T D I T C H   A G O
O   S E I E   R   G
V I O L A   L O A N I N G
E   R L T     T   L
  S T Y L I S T   A B L E
H E Y   O     E S
O D D S   C H I P P A N
U   S I T   D S
S L I P P E D   I N E R T
I   N E I M   V A
N A N   C O N J U R I N G
G   S K G M L   E
```

Solutions

92

```
   S   A E   A C J
W H I N N Y   P O R O U S
   O   G   E   A   E   N
Z E R O   B A R R A C K S
   R   A   T   K   F
A F F A B L Y   N Y L O N
   O   L   D       O
P L U C K   O R C H I D S
   L   H   B   Y       I
D O G E A R E D   K I N D
W   E   I   O   I   I
C O O K E D   C A N I N G
   N   Y   E   K   G   E
```

93

```
  U N O B S T R U C T E D
D   I   U   H   S   O   W
R I G I D   I N E R T I A
E   H   D   N   D   A   R
W I T H H O L D   C L E F
   I   I   Y   B       E
A T E A S E   X R A T E D
L       T   C   O   R
G O A T   S H O W H O M E
E   L   S   O   N   U   D
B U I L T U P   R A P I D
R   B   Y   P   A   E   Y
A L I K E L Y S T O R Y
```

94

```
  D I N N E R J A C K E T
E   N   O E   L   E   U
D I S T O R T   L A Y E R
I   T   K   I U   I   F
T E E M   P R E S E N T
I   A   F   E   I   I
O R D A I N   W O R S E N
N   E   F   N   A   S
  O P I N I O N   O M I T
A   U   D   R   A U   A
C O R G I   M O N G R E L
T   S   S   E   T A   L
S H E P H E R D S P I E
```

95

```
B A N D Y   D I S R O B E
R   R   S   N   E   U
R E V O L T E D   C A F E
N   P   I   E   U   F
P A M P E R   P A R I A H
E       T       L
X M A R K S T H E S P O T
A       T       O
T R I C K Y   R E F U S E
A   Y   L   E   T   E
S C U M   I D E N T I T Y
A   R   N   D   O   U
A S S U A G E   N Y M P H
```

96

```
  A S K A N C E   S W O T
A   K   U   M   I   O
B L U N D E R   A P P L Y
I   L   R   T   C   E   S
D E L T A   S C H O O L
I   W   Y   I   U   P
N O R M A L   S N A T C H
G   E   B   P   E   Y
  P A E L L A   G A N G S
A   S   A   I U   O   I
B L O W N   D Y N A M I C
E   N   K   U   A   S
T U S K   E P I S O D E
```

97

```
H I C C U P   P I N U P
O   O   N   S   O E   E
M A N I A   H I G H E N D
A   T   B   A   O   D   A
G A R L A N D   H Y M N
E   O   T   Y E W   T
  F L U E   I T C H
F   D N A   N   H   H
O U S T   S I N C E R E
R   P   C   I   I C   Y
G A R B L E D   N A K E D
E   I   O   E G   E   A
R I G H T   A S T R A Y
```

98

```
  A   I S E       W   B
B A C K H A N D   T R U E
J   E   O Z   S   E   R
E A C H W A Y   W I N D Y
C   U   Y   M   I   L
T O B Y   S E E P A G E
    E   G       E A
  A S C R I B E   K N O B
A     A   I   S G   I
G R O O M   G R E M L I N
E   N   S   T R   I   A
N U L L   S O U V E N I R
T   Y       E   E G   Y
```

319

Solutions

99

```
  C M   P   C A C
C H O C I C E   A O R T A
A   N   L C   N   C     M
P O T   K H A K I   H O P
I   R       N   S     F
T R A C K S   S T U D I O
U   C   A       E   O   L
L A T E N T   T R O W E L
A       G   H       N   O
T I P   A T O N E   P E W
I   E   R   O   A   O   E
O U T D O   P U R S U E R
N   S   O   S   S   R
```

100

```
S H Y L Y   T W E L F T H
Y   E   O   E   O   O
P E R F U M E D   V A M P
N   T   E   D   E   B
S A L O O N   I N D O O R
    U       N       L
R U S T I C   G A T E A U
P       O       A
P E R S O N   W H I L S T
N   W   S   E   L   A
I D E A   I C E L O L L Y
E   R   G   D   R   V
A D A M A N T   A S T E R
```

101

```
  S   E   L   A P B
S C A M P I   L A R D E R
R   I   F   E E   A
M I N T   E X C U S I N G
P       B     S O
S T E R E O   T O U R   R
S   E   A I R   R   R
    P L O T   A V E N U E
H       A   I       B
A U S T R I A N   R U B Y
R   I   C   E   I   E
C R I N G E   E X P O R T
Y   G   D   S   E   S
```

102

```
H   M R   M E
E A R L O B E S   H U N G
A   A C   P D   E   G
T H I G H   A R R E S T
P   N A   I E   L   E
R A Y S   B R A G G I N G
O   S   S       S   O
O F F S T A G E   S P A M
F   I O   A   S   A
  F L O R A L   P A G A N
J   L E   L   I   E   I
O N U S   G O A L A R E A
Y   P   N   L   C
```

103

```
S H E A T H E   S P U M E
A   S   U S A   A   I
F R E T   F A T A L I T Y
P   R   F   I   R
R O B O T   P R I N C E S
O   N       U E   E
U N F A I R   P A C I F Y
U   E       E O
C O N T A C T   U S A G E
C   E   I   S   H
W E A K E N E D   I R O N
A   I   T   O   T   R
S N I D E   C L O Y I N G
```

104

```
  F C   S   G S C
S L O U G H   R E W O R D
A   L   O   O   A   U
D Y E D   E A U   B U D S
    E   S   C     E
F L A S K   C H I F F O N
I   A D   Y   U   I
P S Y C H I C   A G I L E
T       G   I   I
B L O W   R U M   T U N E
E   A   A E   A   I O
P S A L M S   G I V E U P
S   K   S   E   E   N
```

105

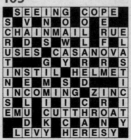

```
  S E E I N G   C O P E
S   V   N   O   O   E
C H A I N M A I L   R U E
R   D   S   W   L   F   L
U S E S   C A S A N O V A
T       G   Y   R   R   S
  I N S T I L   H E L M E T
N   E   M   S D       I
I N C O M I N G   Z I N C
S   L   I   C   R   I
  E M U   C U T T H R O A T
    D   K   C A   N   Y
  L E V Y   H E R E S Y
```

320

Solutions

106

```
R   S   P   W   I   R   B
UNTIL   ARMOURY
N   A   U   S   P   M   W
WORKMATE   COMA
I   B   E   S   U   Y
LOCALE   SPURN
D   A   I   I   E   P
BLANK   GLIDER
L   F   E   N   L   A
ALSO   AUTONOMY
M   K   A   R   V   R   I
BRIDGES   EGGON
S   N   E   E   R   Y   G
```

107

```
S   U   T       G   D
GUNNERS   PLAID
M   M   A   R   O   S
SOFA   NUISANCE
N   S   C   T   O
TELLTALES   PUP
Q   Y   C   P   S   N
PUN   STRUMPETS
A   S   I   D   I
SLIPROAD   NUNS
I   I   N   I   D   O
STOKE   ENCLOSE
Y   Y   G   Y   E
```

108

```
THROWING   SCUT
A   E   I   U   O   Y
CIVILLAW   SNAP
O   U   F   N   F   C   E
BEAU   COOLOFF
B   L   E   R   R   A
AROUND   ACIDIC
D   D   E   I   E   E
BLOSSOM   FEET
L   R   S   P   U   L   U
OBOE   DULLNESS
O   U   R   L   G   E
DUST   DEWYEYED
```

109

```
ESTATEAGENT
O   C   N   U   O   F
TACTIC   FINGER
P   U   O   F   D   E
HOOP   DIATRIBE
P   E   W   I   A
TERMS   SPORT
R   A   S   A   R
PASSWORD   COIL
I   C   N   D   H   C
PANAMA   LOOKAT
E   R   T   E   I   D
LAWANDORDER
```

110

```
T   L   S   G   Q   D
WEIGH   UNUSUAL
I   L   O   I   A   M   O
LAYDOWN   LIMBO
I   T   E   I   Y   K
GANG   BACTERIA
H   O   S   Y   U   P
TESTTUBE   ANTI
Z   E   A   R   S   C
ORDER   UNTWIST
N   I   D   I   E   R   U
ENVIOUS   PRIOR
E   M   E   S   S   E
```

111

```
A   E   P   H   E   I
PUSSYFOOTING
E   T   L   S   E   D   F
SEEKOUT   RHINO
E   N   E   N   G   R
JUMP   ALLALONG
A   S   L   E
BEERTENT   SWOT
B   X   I   U   G   A
EXTOL   DILATED
R   E   T   I   A   E   A
UNCONSIDERED
T   N   M   E   Y   S
```

112

```
C   S   G   S   M   S   W
HUMDRUM   OPERA
A   U   A   O   W   L   X
MAGIC   KUNGFU
E   I   Y   H   C
LOLLOP   TAKETO
E   A   U   L   L   O
OBTUSE   SLAPUP
N   E   I   S   E
SNAKES   POWER
E   E   E   L   I   E   A
BOSSY   ENCHANT
B   S   S   S   E   L   E
```

Solutions

113

```
F   D   N       T A   C
ORIGIN  HUMBLY    L  G
R   S G S   R     L  G
GETSHOTOF    YEN
E   A   T R   R
DESECRATE    OPT
    T   A P   N B
DIE  PAPERCLIP
    I   I O   I L
SOB  MONOLOGUE
H   O   I G   L I
UNWIND  PEANUT
P   L   K     D G Y
```

114

```
CABER    KNOWHOW
A   L O E   U   I E
BIOLOGY    SEPIA
I   A   T   P   P V
NOTE  BAY  YOGI
    E   F D C     N
DERAIL    PUGDOG
Y   G   R B A
NAVE  FUN  DYED
A   I   T L A   U
MANNA    IMPIOUS
I   Y   X N E   N T
CALLING    SAGGY
```

115

```
CAKED    DOGSHOW
A   E R E   A E   O
PAYLOAD    LONER
E   H P U   L N K
ROOK  ACT  RAKI
    L   F T C     N
SWELLS    HUMBUG
U   U F T   O
NAME  CUP  FLIP
R   I I M   W L   O
OWNED    ICEPACK
O   O O N   A R   E
FORELEG    RIDER
```

116

```
    UNWARRANTED
A   A L E   E R   S
MARDI    FITMENT
B   R B U   B C   A
LOANING    ALTER
E   T   E L   L   K
    TEMPO    FLAKE
S   L C     E     E
POLKA    HAMMERS
A   E Y U   I P   S
WHATFOR    GAMMA
N   U V U   C H   Y
    TELLTHETIME
```

117

```
    DEADPAN  SWAB
S   G I G   G A   O
PIOUS    EQUALLY
A   C I   I L   S
RUBDOWN  NICK
I   R   G   E H   P
NEARLY    BAZAAR
G   N I F   R   O
    SCUM  LIGHTER
S   H I A   A     A
PLOTTER  BIGOT
A   U S E   L A   A
TUTU  ADVERSE
```

118

```
T   S S     F R   S
REMATCH  EVENT
A   U   A A   I   U
DUG  BANDSTAND
E   L   D T   T
OLIVE  IDYLLIC
F   N   N N   E   A
FEELING  SHRUG
    X   N L   I   E
CAPACIOUS    FIB
O   E   I V   T A   I
WORDS  ELECTOR
L   T   E     R S   D
```

119

```
    T   A A   S F   W
LIMBERUP  LAID
N   R C O   A L   L
INDUCT  NAKED
E   P I G     E
EDIT  CHECKERS
    L   E
VERYGOOD  EAST
F   F A   P   E
FLUFF  IMBUED
E   N K N   A I
ACID  ENTICING
T   O Y Y   K G
```

Solutions

120

```
 A   I   E   T   S   F
PREMISES    KNOT
 I   B   P   A   I   L
CALICO  REVOKE
     B   U   V   S
APPEASE    PYLON
 I       E   A   N
SCOWL   STRINGY
 K   A   H   N
SMOKED   EFFIGY
 E   I   E   A   E   A
BURN   BIRDCALL
 P   G   T   T   T   E
```

121

```
 OBSCURE    PEAR
S   L   A   E   A   O
HOIST   MILLERS
A   N   S   A   I   T
DYKE   MIXERTAP
Y   E   D   N   L   A
  BROOM   ROCKY
  E   W   L   W   E   S
HEDGEHOG    SCUT
 D   L   G   P   O   U
HINDLEG   LOVED
 C   E   E   A   E   Y
STOW   GRANARY
```

122

```
 FLASH   WORSEN
S   A   C   I   W   A   A
MARKEDMAN   LOG
A   V   P   M   U   I   S
SMART   OSPREY
H   I   R   N
  PEACETREATY
  X   A   A   F
JACKAL   GUSTO
T   C   I   I   E   C   U
OUT   WATERDOWN
M   L   I   Y   L   U   D
BOYISH   MYRRH
```

123

```
P   P   T   S   O   L   C
ILLGOTTEN   IOU
G   E   A   E   C   P   R
LEARNER   ENSUE
E       D   E   A   D
TAP   FOOTBALL
    R   R   Y   V
GOTOSEED   ESS
A   V   X   I   P
GREEN   CANDOUR
E   R   U   I   T   B   A
NUB   MYTHOLOGY
T   S   B   E   F   E   S
```

124

```
 FANCY   EGGON
S   I   A   E   E   P   O
TULIP   MITTENS
E   M   R   B   T   R   I
PRECISE   INANE
S   N   D   N   R
  ITCHY   AGAIN
G   E   I   C   U
REVEL   MAIDENS
I   I   P   P   N   B   H
PROVOKE   SIEGE
E   L   U   L   E   R   R
 SAUTE   STAGE
```

125

```
MASSEUR   CHOIR
I   I   A   E   U   F   E
ACTOR   SKILFUL
O   T   I   S   A
WARTHOG   INBOX
    O   N   N   R   E
STUBBY   HERALD
L   S   O   E   V
OCEAN   NERVOUS
B   E   T   I   A
BREEDER   VALID
E   L   R   A   A   E   L
RUMMY   PILLORY
```

126

```
PLINTH   AFRICA
A   N   A   O   R   V
ETC   SUPERSEDE
L   O   K   O   C   N
LOGO   STEERING
A   N   S   P   F   C   E
  INTRODUCE
I   T   R   U   L   S   S
GEOMETRY   SKIP
N   T   R   I   A   R
INJECTION   TEA
T   A   H   C   E   W
EMBRYO   CHISEL
```

Solutions

127

BICEPS OFFSET
TIMELAPSE AIR
ART UPANDDOWN
ABBEY STATE
SHOWERCAP GUT
DIRTCHEAP
SUGARY CLOSER

128

FISHCAKE WIVES
LOAM HASH CAR
YOKE BONNET
TREMOR SNATCH
HOTDOG CURT
NEAR ABLE
ICING SHREDDED

129

HANDWASH SPAM
RANGE AIRMAIL
HUTU SHANGHAI
BYPASS GRISLY
UNDERWAY OMIT
STUDENT PARKA
DUKE FREEKICK

130

SHIVER SORROW
SWAN USE PITH
SPEECH LOUDLY
SMUGLY TANKER
KNOB AKA DOPE
ACTUAL EXPORT

131

UNCLOG RUBOUT
LEMUR PLOUGH
FACEPACK TUBA
EASY PAINTPOT
ABOUND ENDUP
CROWNS BIGTOP

132

ACIDIC
HANGBACK
ANTI SIEVE TOME
TYPIFY DECANT
ABSENT BADGER
ENVY BARGE LAIR
GREYAREA NOSING

133

GOTHIC UNREAD
SHOUTING NEED
TRIO CHATSHOW
CARFERRY TARN
CHUM MAINSTAY
CLINIC NODULE

Solutions

134

```
  S R POP U S
MUTUAL INDUCE
  D C I T O R
ROCKSALT NEAT
  K S N E   W
AUFAIT DOUBLE
  S C     G A
SICKEN VELVET
  N E A I S
USED BANKNOTE
  U A U I E E
FLORAL TASSEL
  T K ANY S M
```

135

```
PEOPLE CLUTCH
O F I B A S O
DITHERERS USA
I E D R E N R
URN OUTBREAKS
M W H M E
 BRINY AVOID
A I O O L
MADEMONEY HOE
U D A I A Y S
SKI RACEGOERS
E N I E E N E
DOGTAG ESTATE
```

136

```
HOTHOUSE O C
O R C MONTH
VIEW THOU I I
E M O T OAF
RUBY ROTTEN F
 L W L E O
PHYSIO BRITON
A N P S I
I TAKEON OPAL
DUO I L P L
O P NOIR FLEA
FLING S E M
F C CHARISMA
```

137

```
 V T P A W B
SAMOSA PAIRUP
P X YAP P D
WIFI B A EASE
D CRAWLER D
 A C Y END
G RACKETEER Y
EFT O O R
R JOINTED S
MEMO N A OAKS
V U GEL U U
DIESEL LASTLY
L T E Y E L
```

138

```
E L U S C A
LAYING ONLOAN
E R H S E A D
CHASE CLASSY
T A A K T R
REVERING FETA
I O D F R I
FEUD INPRISON
Y C S O A C
CHUTES MOTTO
I E R E E O A
MORTAR PULPIT
P S P P I S
```

139

```
 A F F B A A
INDIVIDUALIST
O S R G S S
RICHES BROGUE
N T T E M
ATLAS SAYWHEN
 N I R O
ROCKING BRISK
P F I K O
STANZA SURELY
I U N S A A
POETICJUSTICE
N S Y E E E
```

140

```
 ADAGE SMIRK
S A O I U I C
PLYWOOD SAMBA
R S D Y I R
ITCH PLACEMAT
N H C L B U
TROPHY CONCUR
 O I S X K A
POLITICS PRIG
U C O O A I
MULCH PIGSKIN
P O A E L E G
 FORTY BEARD
```

325

Solutions

141

```
. D . A . H . S . H .
T U R N U P . U N T R U E
. C . S . O . R . R . N
S K E W . L E T T I N G S
. E . O . S . P . O . .
S T O R A G E . H E A V Y
. W . . Y . Q . . . E .
F O G G Y . C U T L E R Y
. P . R . S . A . O . .
C I V I L W A R . V O L T
. E . M . I . T . E . A
S C A L E S . E R R A N T
. E . Y . H . T . S . D
```

142

```
. B I R D S E Y E V I E W
E . N . E . G . P . R . H
M O C H A . O R I G A M I
I . E . D . I . C . T . S
T U N E L E S S . S E C T
. S . O . M . S . . . L .
G R E A S E . S P R I T E
E . S . H . R . L . . . .
T O S S . S O C A L L E D
O . A . O . R . Y . W . A
V O U C H E R . G U I L D
E . N . M . O . U . L . O
R E A S S U R I N G L Y .
```

143

```
. O V E R W H E L M I N G
A . I . A . I . E . N . O
S E A T I N G . A N N U L
K . D . D . H . V . E . D
A B U T . A L G E B R A .
N . C . C . Y . O . E . .
C I T R U S . P U N C H Y
E . . L . G . T . A . E .
H E A D B O Y . P L U S .
S . X . E . S . W . Y . O
O P A L S . S K I P P E R
F . C . A . I . L . S . E
A N T I C I P A T I O N .
```

144

```
T A S T Y . T R I B U T E
R . I . S . E . L . U . .
D E S E R T E D . E C R U
N . D . U . M . E . M . .
B A B O O N . E M P L O Y
. . W . . . A . . . I . .
N O N N E G O T I A B L E
I . . . O . . . C . . . .
S L I C E D . R E C I T E
D . Y . L . I . U . I . .
C R A M . E X C U S E M E
U . . R . S . K . E . E .
I M P U L S E . A D O R N
```

145

```
. A S C E T I C . T S A R
S . T . M . F . P . U . .
P R E S S U P . A D U L T
I . A . T . O . V . N . S
D E L T A . S P O T O N .
E . . B . E . U . U . Z .
R U F F L E . W R I T H E
S . I . E . T . A . . A .
. S T Y M I E . B A B E L
U . N . A . M . L . L . O
S P E L T . P R E V E N T
E . . S . E . E . . N . S
D O S E . P R O V I D E .
```

146

```
. C R A V I N G . S T E P
H . E . E . E . C . O . O
I N V E R S E . O N A I R
R . U . I . D . N . S . K
S H E A F . L E V I T Y .
U . . I . E . E . E . O .
T H W A C K . H Y B R I D
E . A . A . P . O . . Y .
. G R O T T O . R A C E S
W . B . I . P . B . H . S
I G L O O . P E E R A G E
R . E . N . E . L . I . Y
E A R N . O R A T O R Y .
```

147

```
. D E B A S E . O B T A I N
A . A . P . A . E . N . O
T O F F E E S . L I K E N .
E . F . N . K . I . L . S
. F L I T . E Y E T E S T .
H . E . W . V . . . I . .
O R D A I N . H E C T I C .
N . . . T . O . . . O . K
O N B O A R D . P I P S . .
U . I . L . D . A . S . U
R A B B I . L E S S O N S .
E . L . C . Y . T . I . E
D R E S S Y . E A G L E S .
```

Solutions

148

```
CLOSED STRIDE
A E R I E I
OPENCAST LOVE
S S U I I
MENU GENOCIDE
A H E
WELLTHUMBED
I N A
SNEAKING NORM
E S V O G U
AGES OLDFLAME
U E R L E B
SMITHY YESMAN
```

149

```
Z U B P F S
ORPHAN FULLUP
D H C S R A R
ICESKATER WHO
A A D R O U
COVERNOTE AFT
A O N C M
PAL POGOSTICK
A A T C I
NIB FIREALARM
D U O M T B O
EATOUT FILLIN
R T L C Y O
```

150

```
RAVAGE CLIMB
A I E S O N E
TOLET HASBEEN
T L A A Y P I
LEATHER STAG
E G E KEG N
FETA ROUT
P DNA A T S
RAFT SOCIETY
O I B H I N S
FOXHOLE ONSET
I E N S U I E
TODAY ASYLUM
```

151

```
S D C A A B
PROPHESY KNEE
I O U T T T R
CURATOR HAIRY
E P E A E L
SHOW SYRINGE
S T R O
STIRFRY ABLE
S I I S A V
MAGIC PANACHE
I I K P A K N
LIFT BLURTOUT
E T E E N S
```

152

```
S O D F S P
CLIMBER ALTAR
O N O E R Y O
MUG EAGLE ELF
P U S W I
UNLOCK REDHOT
T A O L O M
ENRICH PLASMA
R K S E R
ICY SANDY PIG
S O U A A I I
EAGER KINGPIN
D A E K E
```

153

```
DAUBS BECAUSE
V R E N T K
DEPARTED TOYS
R V C M I B
ATTACH ONCALL
D S U
AFLOAT TICKET
O E H
BURSAR FLASHY
N A R A M O
IDOL INCUBATE
R V F T E U
SYNONYM GRAPH
```

154

```
C S S O C B
SUBMIT WHORLS
R O A E M U
STAG INDEMAND
A R U T
LIQUOR TUTU
N S ONO E T
LEAD ELDEST
T D C H
PUBCRAWL COIL
D A I A R
SOARED PIRATE
R S E S S
```

Solutions

155

```
A   S S     G A
FOUNTAIN  MUST
F  S   E   M N M
EXUDE   SMUDGE
C  A D   T R H B
TOLL  PARANOIA
I   F     L   R
OVERLAND  SCAR
N  T  U A S O I
 SHRIMP  MANIC
W  I D K A G A
HACK  PILCHARD
Y  S     N K
```

156

```
HEATING   SPADE
 A   A  E A A  R
TREK  SCREWCAP
 T   E  S  R   I
PHASE  COMMEND
 L   T    W  O
BYROAD  SHODDY
 C   I     T  I
BOOKISH  SPASM
 P   M  T  O H
PINKLADY  IRON
 U   I  L R  N U
AMITY  RESTATE
```

157

```
 S  H B  S S B
STROBE  TAWDRY
 A  L R  R I E
BRED  EAU  MEET
 O  T  D   C
ABOVE  HEALTHY
 O  E F  L A E
SMARTLY  TWIST
 B   O A C
USED  URN  OATH
 I O   N G U O
ATOMIC  SORDID
 E  E Y T T L
```

158

```
TINGED   MOPE
G  N  E R A  L
RACETRACK  ARC
A  U S W E T A
MARE  ZEROHOUR
O  J R V O R
POWWOW  LEANTO T
H H I H R   T
ORIENTAL  ZINC
N  T E T E R A
EAT  DIRTYWORK
 L U  E E N E
LEAP  DESIST
```

159

```
C  P M S T T A
HALVA  TOWERED
A  E R  I O I
TRACKING  SPAR
E   E K P O E
ASTUTE  CURVE
U  I I  P E F
 GRAND  SPIRAL
P  E G S Y A
RIDE  SHELVING
O  O E A O R G
VAULTED  VOICE
E  T C E E S D
```

160

```
M  F G   C B
HURRIED  THROB
S  A  T D E W
SKIN  AMICABLE
 K  F S P O
AFFLUENCE  PVC
 I Y  E E A E
TRY  FLORISTRY
 E  S F N P
BROCCOLI  INNS
 I O R B R U
USEUP  PLAINLY
 K T  E N L
```

161

```
ALLEGORY  DISC
R  U O E   L L
TAPEDECK  FLEA
Y  I O I B E A
 GNAW  PARAGON
W   N E A A I
APATHY  PSALMS
 T D I U S H
ENVELOP  EACH
R  A L R D H P
JUNE  MONORAIL
U  C  A F F U
GREY  DRIFTERS
```

328

Solutions

162

```
D  S  L     P  I     F
D  E  N  T  R  Y     S  U  C  C  U  M  B
M     A  I     Y  E  L  L
O  R  G  A  N  I  C     C  E  L  L  O
R     G  H     U  F  C
A  K  I  N     J  E  T  B  L  A  C  K
L     N  Q     E  C  B
I  N  T  R  U  D  E  R     H  E  R  O
S     R  A  R     A     O
I  D  E  A  L     M  U  D  P  A  C  K
N     P  I     D  X  I
G  L  I  S  T  E  N     U  N  I  O  N
   D  Y  E  P  S  G
```

163

```
A  A  A     V  I  I
B  A  R  N  S  T  O  R  M  I  N  G
U  C  I  T     P  J  M
T  W  A  D  D  L  E     A  R  O  M  A
N  E  I  L     K  K  R
P  I  E  R     K  N  E  E  J  E  R  K
A     B     D     E
S  W  A  L  L  O  W  S     A  G  E  D
T  F  I     A  S  L
E  L  F  I  N     T  E  N  U  O  U  S
L  R  D  E     I  O  A
T  A  I  L  O  R  S  D  U  M  M  Y
Y  Y     Y  E  Y  S
```

164

```
D  E  F  U  S  E     T  O  U  C  A  N
E  R  U     S  R     H  U
P  R  I  O  R  T  O     G  U  A  R  D
I  A  F     L  A  R  I
C  O  R  G  I     V  A  N  D  A  L  S
T  N  E     D  T
   U  S  A  G  E     S  T  E  E  P
H  N  D  R  C
A  V  I  A  T  O  R     A  F  T  E  R
N  F  H  A  V  I     E
G  A  F  F  E     P  L  E  A  T  E  D
U  L  R  E  L  L  I
P  R  E  S  E  T     A  S  C  E  N  T
```

165

```
U     A  F  E     S  S  I
U  S  E  T  A  L  I  G  H  T     A  R  M
U  T  U  G  A  R  A
R  E  A  L  M     N  E  T  T  I  N  G
P  C  M  O  E  I
   T  H  R  O  U  G  H     F  L  A  N
P  E  X  O  U  E
O  D  D  S     E  D  I  F  I  C  E
R  K  R  F  K  T
C  H  U  T  N  E  Y     B  U  Y  E  R
I  R  A  R  E  D  U
N  A  G     V  I  O  L  A  T  I  O  N
E  E  E  T  T  P  K
```

166

```
D  I  S  P  L  A  Y  C  A  S  E
N  O  U     A  T     E
T  E  A  P  O  T     S  T  I  C  K  Y
R  P  U  I  F  E
S  T  A  Y     M  A  N  O  F  G  O  D
N     N  O  E  P
L  E  A  F  Y     A  N  N  E  X
S     R  I  O  N
E  S  T  E  E  M  E  D     T  E  E  M
M  E  P  D  E  N
M  U  E  S  L  I     S  T  E  A  D  Y
Y  I  S  O  N  E
   W  A  S  H  I  N  G  S  O  D  A
```

167

```
A  E  P     S  B  W  A
N  O  D  O  U  B  T     O  V  E  R  T
A  E  L  O  L  A  E
R  E  N  A  L     N  O  T  A  R  Y
C  R  Y     D  A
H  U  B  C  A  P     A  B  R  O  A  D
I  O  N  L  W  V
S  P  O  O  K  Y     F  I  A  N  C  E
M  K  M  N  R
   U  S  A  B  L  E     K  I  N  G  S
E  H  O  R  E  E  E
S  M  O  K  Y     C  U  R  E  A  L  L
P  P  S  Y  S  R  Y
```

168

```
R  F  S        F  S  S
A  L  L  O  U  T     B  U  C  K  E  T
S  Y  R  C  R  I  E
H  O  P  E  F  U  L  L  Y     P  E  W
E  A  A  O  E
R  E  P  A  C  K  A  G  E     P  O  D
E  E  K  L  R
T  O  R     D  I  R  T  I  N  E  S  S
A  O  G  S  U
K  E  Y     P  R  O  V  I  D  E  N  T
E  O  I  M  B  R  U
U  N  K  I  N  D     C  L  O  V  E  R
P  E  K     E  E  E
```

329

Solutions

169

```
W A F E R   C A L C I U M
I   L   E   H O   R   E
D A Y C A R E   G R O A N
E   P   D   E   O   N   T
N O O N   D R Y   M Y T H
    S   S   S   W       O
C A T C H Y   S H R I L L
L   Y   S   Y   N       L
O W L S   A P P   C R O W
S   I   L   O   L O   E
E N T R Y   I M I T A T E
U   R   R   L   M D   K
P R E H E A T   B U S E S
```

170

```
F I F T Y   B A C K R O W
A   I   E   L   L   I   I
C O N C A V E   A P P A L
E   D   R   W   N   E   L
D R O P   D U G   A N T I
    U   H   P   G       N
H O T P O T   T Y P I N G
E       W   S   M   M
L O B E   A T M   S P O T
L   A   E   R   C   O   W
I N L E T   I N H O U S E
S   S   U   N   I   N   E
H E A R I N G   C A D E T
```

171

```
  I N D E X L I N K E D
C   O   A   O   O V   S
L O S E R   W I T H O U T
I   T   L   K   E   K   A
F O R E S E E   P L E A T
F   I       Y   A     E
  B L A C K   C D R O M
L     O   S   V   P
A L B U M   C O R T E G E
Y   R   I   O   E R   A
B O U N C E R   S H A C K
Y   T   A   C   I R   S
  T E L L T H E T I M E
```

172

```
C A S T O F F   O C H E
S   L   A   I   R   A R
T R I C K L E   A P R O N
I   G   E   R   C   T   E
C O N G A   C L I P O N
K   F   E   N   O   S
U N R E A L   A G E N C Y
P   A   N   E   D   N
  S I T C O M   R A T I O
U   D   Y   E   I O   N
S W E E T   R E V E L R Y
E   R   O   G   E L   M
D A S H   H E I R E S S
```

173

```
D E V I C E   C U R L U P
O   E   R   B   N   A   A
G E N T E E L   D O N O R
S   T   A   R   E     T
  P U N K   D E E P S E T
T   R   E   S       I
A V E N U E   A S Y L U M
X   N   A   U     E
I N N I N G S   P O R E
R   I   E   I   O C   L
A N G E R   D E A T H L Y
N   H   V   E   C E   N
K I T T E N   T H O R A X
```

174

```
K I T B A G   H O B B L E
  C   R   L   Y   R   E
F I N E T U N E   O V A L
  L   W   T   N   O   R
T Y R E   T R A C K I N G
      R   O       E
  F L Y I N G S Q U A D
  U       E       N
B R I D G I N G   S U M P
T   O   M   M   O   O
T H U D   P R E J U D G E
E   G   L   N       U
B R E E Z Y   T I D I L Y
```

175

```
  C   S   M     R   A   U
R E P E A L   F U N R U N
O   R   G   E   N   A   F
U N I O N F L A G   L E O
C   N   E   A       L
H I G H T A B L E   C A D
E   I   O   M   R
S I R   C E R T I T U D E
O       A   S   D   X
R I M   G O T O S L E E P
T   E   U   E   I O   E
E N A B L E   L O T I O N
D   N   P   N   L   D
```

330

Solutions

176
```
T O P K N O T   S T U D
D   P   H   B   S   A   A
E X T R A   L O Y A L T Y
F   K   I   N   L   S
U P S W I N G   T U S K
N   T   E   A   T   S
C O E R C E   E X P O R T
T   E   O   S   R   A
  B L U R   C A R R Y O N
A   W   D   A   E   D
B L O T O U T   A L I B I
L   O   N   T   C   O   N
Y U L E   P Y T H O N S
```

177
```
S   C   K     T   W   G
T R A C I N G   O T H E R
R   R   S   O   S   O   I
E S P   S N O W S T O R M
A   E   D   U   P
M U S E S   F O P P I S H
E   T   O   N   E
R O I S T E R   D O G M A
    M   O   T   R   D
S C U L P T U R E   W I G
A   L   P   N   A   A   I
G R U E L   E A R L I E R
E   S   E     Y   L   L
```

178
```
  P   I   C   B   T   C
C H E N I L L E   A H O Y
R   N   E   N   X   S
V A L U E R   I D I O M
S   E   I   G   I
F E R N   C O N T R I C K
D       O       O
C A N O P I E D   L O C K
D   N   E   Y   O
V I R U S   V A P O U R
I   A   E   I   O   R
A S T I   R E S T L E S S
E   D   T   E   Y   E
```

179
```
K   G   S   E   A   J
U N W O R T H Y   R O O T
E   L   E   E   M   G
M E A D O W   S L O G A N
    E   P   U   L
A B A N D O N   C R O O K
E   T   S   N
T E M P T   U P S T A G E
T   E   A   R
P L A T E D   R A I S I N
I   I   I   T   L   D
G N A T   S E A T B E L T
G   E   H   N   Y   Y
```

180
```
S   S   S     S   S
I N B U I L T   M U M P S
O   M   U   C   C   I
S W I M   M A R C H I N G
Y   O   I   D
  K N O C K S   H U L K
O   U   A   I   U   Y
S N I P   R E S O R T
G   B   D   S
W O R S E O F F   L I K E
I   A   N   L   I
S N A C K   B U R N I N G
G   K   X   G   S
```

181
```
  A G I L I T Y   B O M B
S   A   U   O   O   O
P E T E R   F O R G I V E
A   E   K   F   I   I
R A M P   D E M O B B E D
K   O   H   E   T   A
S N O U T   V E I N S
E   B   B   R   K   S
L A Y A B O U T   S C U M
V   U   N   Z   L   I
B E A N B A G   I N E R T
R   U   L   N   R   H
S T U B   T E A C A K E
```

182
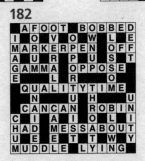
```
  A F O O T   B O B B E D
I   O   V   O   W   L   E
M A R K E R P E N   O F F
A   U   R   P   U   S   T
G A M M A   O P P O S E
E   L   R   O
  Q U A L I T Y T I M E
N   U   H   U
C A N C A N   R O B I N
C   I   A   I   O   L   I
H A D   M E S S A B O U T
U   E   E   T   T   W   Y
M U D D L E   L Y I N G
```

331

Solutions

183

```
E   B   A   A   A   U   S
GOLDMINER     NAP
O   O   B   I   C   B   I
INTERIM   HOIST
S       O   A       A   E
MET   SELFLESS
    A   I       O   E
  PLEASING   DIG
S   K       N   C       R
CIDER   FRAGILE
O   U   U   B   C   A
RAW   BOSSINESS
E   N   Y   E   N   D   E
```

184

```
FLAMBE   WOLVES
I   R   A   S   W   I   H
CLEARUP   ISSUE
K   N   R   I   N   C   I
LLAMA   LEGWORK
E       G   L       U   H
  SPEED   SLUSH
C   E       E   A       G
LEANING   NOBLE
O   S   D   G   T   L   N
SHOAL   OVEREAT
E   U   E   N   R   A   L
REPORT   KNOTTY
```

185

```
  SPIKE   USUAL
A   A   I   T   M   U   M
DOYEN   BROADLY
A   M   G   O   K   I   R
PRESSON   INTER
T   N       E   N       H
  STICK   AGREE
S   P   R   P   L   A
PLAZA   RANGERS
I   L   C   I   I   M   T
CLOAKED   CREPE
Y   U   L   E   H   N   R
  ADDER   MEATY
```

186

```
VISITOR   FLIRT
O   I   H   E   L   O   O
UTTER   SEAGULL
C       O   I   C       I
HANDBAG   CORGI
    U       N   I   H
SCRUBS   EDGING
I   S   I   A       N
CHEST   TELLOFF
K       P   T   A       A
PETNAME   RABBI
A   E   R   N   V   E   R
YEAST   DRAPERY
```

187

```
WIDELY   SWELLS
O   E   A   O   I   P
REV   IMPROMPTU
T   I   R   O   D   R
HEAD   BLACKOUT
Y   T   A   A   H   B   S
  IMPARTIAL
A   O   O   B   P   I   L
MINISTER   OGLE
U   T   A   E   A   E
STEELDRUM   TOW
E   L   E   I   E   A
DEFUSE   STODGY
```

188

```
TRENDS   CHASER
E   V   E   P   E   C   A
DEADLYSIN   AID
I   D   I   A   N   R   I
USE   VALUABLES
M       E   M       E   H
  SMIRK   BOOTH
B   A       S   L       R
UNINVITED   SEA
F   L   I   A   H   P   G
FIB   SAILALONG
E   A   I   D   N   O   E
TIGHTS   ADDLED
```

189

```
DECORATE       S   A
I   O       A   HOPES   S
GALL   ALGA   R   S
U   L       C   R   AKA
PEAK   PUNDIT       U
    G   S   M   H       L
GREENS   BANDIT
R       I   S   T   R
A   BEGGAR   LICK
TOO   G   L       P   N
I   T   EVIL   EDGE
FLOUR   V       R   A
Y   X   HAWKEYED
```

Solutions

190

```
W H I S P E R S   S C U T
I   N   A   I   P   L   I
N O T E D   B A R N O W L
C   E   B   O   U   L
H I G H   C O N F E T T I
    E   B   N   A   I   N
B A R R E D   E N D I N G
O   E   P   E   N
T E A B R E A K   V E R B
T   D   M   G   R   L
L U M B A G O   O U T D O
E   I   T   D   A   I   C
D A T E   B A C K P A C K
```

191

```
  G   K   S   S   A   F
B R A N C H   M A G G O T
  O   I   O   O   A   R
S W O T   W O K   R I G S
  U   E   E   E
S P I D E R   R I V E R S
  N           O
A F F A I R   B E W A R E
  I   E   A   E
E D E N   G U N   W E F T
  D   E   A   G   O   U
A L K A L I   E N O U G H
  E   T   N   R   L   E
```

192

```
S   T   E   B W   W
E X H A L E   B R O O C H
L   U   A   L   O   R   Y
F I G H T   I N T A K E
I   I   M   H   I   P
M A N T O M A N   A N T I
A   A   N   C   G   L
G A I N   C A R O U S E L
E   L   P   I   U   A
  A D O R E D   N E V E R
A   O   I   E   T   I   B
S E W I N G   B O L E R O
K   N   T   N   W   X
```

193

```
S I E N N A   C   S   I
N   E   T R U C K I N G
I D L E   T   R   I   B
U   D R A W L   M O O N
C   C   C   E   R
S T A R C H   R O V I N G
U           I
E M I G R E   F E N D E R
A       S   A   I   T
P R O W   T O U C H   E
G   O   A   L   A   C H E
H I T O U T A T   N   E
N   D   E   Y O G U R T
```

194

```
  A   L E   B S   B
U N S O L D   O C C U L T
  G   W   I   R   A   I
P O L L U T E D   R A G E
  R   Y   E       H
T A X I   P A R A S I T E
  N   H   O   E
F L A G D O W N   T I D Y
  E   N   T   E
S M U G   E N V E L O P E
  O   A   B   I   E   U
I N D I G O   C R U S T Y
  S   T   X   E   P   Y
```

195

```
  P   R   E S P   F   S
C A R I N G   O C L O C K
  E   P   G   T   O   U
S L I P K N O T   P U L P
  L   L   O   E       P
F A C I N G   D E M O T E
  O   N   A       A
G I N G E R   R E T O R T
  N       U   E   E   E
U S E D   M A V E R I C K
  U   I   P   E   I   T
P L U R A L   R E A S O N
  T   T   E Y E   L   R
```

196

```
E C L A I R   D E G R E E
L   O   C   E   A   A   V
D E C R E A S E S   D Y E
E   U   D   T   E   I   N
S U M   B O O T L A C E S
T   U   P   A   O
  S W I N G   I D Y L L
N   E       C   E       P
I N T H E B U F F   A G A
S   T   N   R   R   R   R
S K I   D I S C O V E R S
E   N   U   E   S   C   O
N U G G E T   S T R A I N
```

Solutions

197

198

199

200

201

202

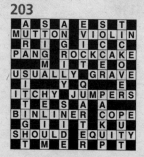

203

Solutions

204

```
  F I R E M A N S L I F T
F   N   X   N   U   V   E
O P E R A   T O M B O L A
U   P   M   L   P   R   C
R E T A I N E R   M Y T H
    L   N   R   P       E
M A Y H E M   D R I V E R
E   R   P   I   E
L O P E   B E S M I R C H
O   E   A   L   E   T   I
D E C I B E L   C R I C K
I   A   E   E   U   G   E
C O N S T I T U T I O N
```

205

```
  B O M B E R J A C K E T
P   P   E   E   L   E   A
H A U L A G E   A B Y S S
Y   L   D   V   R   I   K
S U E T   S E E M I N G
I   N   L   S   I       E
C O T T O N   U N I S E X
S   N   T   G   A   P
  E P I G R A M   E V I L
E   A   S   C   G   I   O
T O R C H   T W O F O L D
C   K   O   I   W   U   E
H E A L T H C E N T R E
```

206

```
S P A T E   I M M E N S E
R   I   S   O   A   A
F I L M S T A R   G O N G
V   E   U   O   E   D
B Y W O R D   C H R O M E
    F       C   C   A
C O F F E E M O R N I N G
V   M               A
S E N D U P   A L M O S T
R   O   O   W   E   W
R A N I   W E A R T H I N
R   N   E   Y   A   R
I M A G E R Y   A G I L E
```

207

```
E M P R E S S   A B L E
B   I   U   L   R   Y
R O S E H I P   I R A T E
E   E   E   P   P   V   S
A O R T A   L I S T E D
K   D   E   E   R   U
I N C I T E   C R A Y O N
N   E   O   S   V   T
  A N T H E M   I N C U R
U   S   E   A   C   H   U
S A U N A   R E E L E C T
E   R   D   M   S   H
D U E L   C Y C L I S T
```

208

```
S M O O T H   T A C I T
T   F   R   S   I   L   I
R I F L E   C O N C E R N
O   P   K   O   Y   A   G
B R E A K U P   O R A L
E   A   I   E T C     Y
  S K I N   R U S K
C   G A S   I   W   O
H I P S   P A C K E R S
O   R   S   A   K   L   P
S L A P P E D   E N T E R
E   W   R   E   T   E   E
N A N N Y   A S T R A Y
```

209

```
O   P   A   E       O   S
D E R I D I N G   S P I N
D   I   U   Z   F   A   O
S A V E L O Y   R U L E R
O   A   T   M   O       E
N U T S   R E C T I F Y
    E   W       H   A
A S T O U N D   M I N I
C   U   I   F   R   M
H A V E N   B R I N G U P
I   A   D   B   L   A   O
P O S T   O L D T I M E R
S   T   E       H   E   T
```

210

```
    H   O S   W   A   B
P L A Y B O Y   A M B E R
E   R   O R   T   U   E
R I D   E X U D E   T O W
S   S   P   R       E
O P E N L Y   G L O W E R
N   L   E   O   E   S
A F L O A T   V O L L E Y
L   L   R   S   L   E
I L L   N A M E D   D N A
S   I   I   O   A   O   S
E L F I N   C O R O N E T
D   T   G   K   N   E
```

335

Solutions

211

```
A C U T E   S H A D O W Y
  H   R   A   A     E   E
M I X E D B A G   B E A T
  N   K   L   G   U   R
L A C K E Y   A U T H O R
      E           R   U
F O U R T H   D E B A T E
  B       E   U
P E N C I L   D R O P B Y
  S   A   P   U   Y   A
L I M P   I N S T A N C E
  T   R   N   K   N   O
S Y R I N G E   S T I N T
```

212

```
  S   A M   B T   S
K U N G F U   A T O N C E
  P   E   T   L   O   E
S P U D   T H I C K E N S
  E       O       O   E
G R O C E R   S A V E
  S   R   E L M   E   S
    L E N D   E R R A N D
  F   P   L       L   I
F R E E F A L L   L O V E
  A   R   U   I   U   E
F U S I O N   N I C E L Y
  D   E   T   G   K   S
```

213

```
W     S   E     T G
H A U N T I N G   P R A Y
I   N   O   I D   Y   M
T A L O N   G E R B I L
E   I   E   M O N   I
F A T E   S A L V A G E S
I   S       E       O
S P E A K I N G   V E A L
H   V   U   I B   L
  J E T L A G   R I V E T
A   N   K G A   E   I
M A U L   C L O S E R U N
P   P     E H
```

214

```
I C E B E R G   H Y D R O
  A   R   I   A   E   E
F R E E   L O N G W A V E
  P   A   E   Y   E
R O C K Y   C O U R T L Y
  O   E       N   E
S L I V E R   E N C A S E
  E   A       U   T
T E E N A G E   G R O U T
  X   L   V   R   N
S I M U L A T E   I N N S
  S   R   N   E   N   E
S T U N T   B R I G A D E
```

215

```
  C   W   N   C K   C
C H I R P Y   H A N G O N
  I   I M   E   O   M
G N A T   P V C   W I P E
      E   H   K       A
I G L O O   L I B R A R Y
  R   F   C   N   A   E
H O T F O O T   K I O S K
  U       M   D N
S T A B   P I E   D A N K
  I   E   I   R   O   A
S N I V E L   B O W T I E
  G   Y   E   Y N   L
```

216

```
M O S A I C   M I S T
P   P   R   O   A     T
A F A S T B U C K   A K A
S   L   Y   P E   L   I
T A S K   C O W O R K E R
M   U   N   V   E     F
A L M O N D   R E A D E R
S   O   U   T   R     E
T U N G S T E N   M A X I
E   S   A   A T   M   G
R O T   B A C K S L A S H
    E   L   U   A   S   T
  T R E E   P E R I S H
```

217

```
B   I   D   S E   B B
R A D I I   T U M B L E R
A   E   F   A U   O   I
C O A L F A C E   S W A B
K       I K   F   O   E
E F F E C T   C A R V E
N   I   U   U   E S
  D R I L L   F L U R R Y
G   E   T   P T       M
L E E K   F U L L S T O P
O   X   S T   E   O   T
  B R I S K E T   S A L V O
E   T   Y   Y   S   L   M
```

336

Solutions

218

```
 H P N . M S .
 SUBSOIL PUMPS
 S Y P S S R .
 CHIC IRISHJIG
 . H N L Y N .
 PLAINTIVE ATM
 I C H E S E .
 EBB SEARCHERS
 E O A B A .
 GRAFFITI KIWI
 A F R R E I .
 BLEAK ACQUIRE
 S L H P Y .
```

219

```
 FLIPSIDE EPIC
 U N O I E A
 MONKFISH KNOB
 E E T A P G L
 PROP REHOUSE
 T A M O I C
 AWHILE STANZA
 X A A A O R
 EXCITED GIST
 X K E J R H L
 ICED COMATOSE
 L R I P C A
 EASY UNSHAKEN
```

220

```
 EFFECTIVELY
 O N U I E T
 CONSUL RIGOUR
 T U I I E E
 SHOE POLONECK
 I S E D O
 GLADE PSALM
 L O S A D
 ISOLATED WICK
 D E I R I R
 LAWFUL INDEED
 Y U T F T A
 CLOSETOHOME
```

221

```
 S G A A G P
 NEEPS SCREECH
 O N I S A R E
 WHEEDLE MOCHA
 B E S M E L
 OVER ESCAPIST
 A N E R V H
 RATTLING DEAR
 D R I E K E
 INERT CONFESS
 N A I T O N O
 GOTOSEA COVER
 Y M R K Y T
```

222

```
 W C A A D P
 IRRESISTIBLE
 S E H S A M
 PLATEAU PASTA
 T S R U M R
 REEL LEFTBACK
 A L E E E
 BADLYOFF SWOT
 I O E I S R
 EIGHT NEWNESS
 S T E E T I
 MASSPRODUCED
 G T Y E H E
```

223

```
 U C B A I B B
 SLURRED DAISY
 E B O D L R E
 BASIC OVERDO
 Y C N B W
 DEPLOY SALAMI
 A A L Q T N
 TUNEIN HUSHED
 E T C A C
 SHOWER ROACH
 A E A A L I
 TARRY COUNSEL
 E S S K S O L
```

224

```
 ISIS ROSETTE
 H O E T R L
 BONSAI ORATOR
 R K O D P
 STABLING EYES
 E O E M
 ANGORA SWATCH
 K R R U
 CLOT STARKERS
 E O E D A
 BANKON DROPBY
 S E A E A L
 HANDLED KEEP
```

Solutions

225

```
  S   T P   S M   Z
B I K I N I   C R I T I C
  N   P G   R G   N
Z E R O   G R A P H I C S
  C   F E   M T
G U N F I R E   N Y M P H
  R     Y A P     A
B E A R D   R U B B I N G
  O     P   T E   D
B A R T E R E D   C O A X
  R   A U   O O   C
S I F T E D   W O M B A T
  D   E E   N E   R
```

226

```
A C H I E V E   O V A L S
N   O   A M   V K   L
G U M   T A B L E W A R E
S   E   S L   R   N
T O G A   D E S P I S E D
    R   N M   L L
C O O P E R   L A B O U R
R   W   U D   Y U
U N N E R V E D   S C U M
N   O   C I   H E
C O A T S T A N D   I L L
H   I   I M   O N   O
Y A R N S   P O L Y G O N
```

227

```
  F   S G   E F   L
B R I C K R E D   I C E D
  A   Y A   I L   A
E M I T   P O T P L A N T
  E   H E   I U   T
U D D E R   S O A P B O X
  U   K   N   R
L O O K I N G   S C A L Y
  U   I E   W H   U
S T A M P E D E   E A S Y
  R   O P   A E   T
B U R N   A D V I S O R Y
  N   O D   E E   E
```

228

```
C O B W E B   T E T H E R
O   A   A B   N U   E
I D L E R   R E V E R I E
N   S   L U   O D   K
C H A M O I S   Y O L K
I   B   H   E   W
D O T T E D   S W E R V E
E   R   S R   L
  J O L T   P A I N F U L
S   U   H A   N E   K
C O N T E N D   K N I F E
U   C   I E   L G   P
T H E O R Y   C Y G N E T
```

229

```
E T H I C S   S T I F L E
U   I L   A I   I
L A P S E D   B U L L E T
O H   F R U I T   I H
G O O D   U R   K N E E
Y   P R O M P T I N G   R
    Y   S H E
P   S E C T A R I A N   S
A F A R   I A   D U C T
R   C   A C U T E   M E
S H R I N K   E D I B L E
O   E T   I E   L
N U D I S M   S T A R R Y
```

230

```
S C O P E   S C R U F F Y
R   R   T O   N   I
K I L O G R A M   L E F T
S   B   A P   E T
U P W A R D   U N T I E
    T   E T   E
T R U E   D I E   F O N D
I   E   R R
  G R U F F   G L I T C H
H   R   I A   L R
S T U B   C O M P L A I N
O   A   I E   E M
I N A N I T Y   E D G E D
```

231

```
K N E E C A P   S H A R D
I   N A   I K   R   E
B E V E L   T H E R M O S
B   E F   C L   E I
L I L T   S H E E P D O G
E   O   W E   T   N
  U P S A N D D O W N S
S   R   B N   O F
H I G H R O A D   S U M O
O   A   I T   T R   R
W A L K O U T   S L I N G
E   E R   L A   S E
R I S E S   E A R S H O T
```

Solutions

232

```
V E T O ■ D R E S S E R
■ P ■ A ■ I X ■ I ■ O ■
M I S F I T ■ P E N T U P
■ S ■ ■ T ■ E ■ C ■ N ■
S T U B B O R N ■ E D D Y
■ L ■ R ■ S ■ R ■ ■ ■ ■
B E G I N S ■ E N E R G Y
■ G ■ ■ E ■ L I ■ L ■ ■
P L E A ■ C A R R Y O F F
■ O ■ D ■ R ■ E ■ ■ T ■
I G N I T E ■ P U R I T Y
■ I ■ E ■ T L ■ A ■ A ■
■ C A R V E R Y ■ W A G E
```

233

```
T U C K I N G ■ C R U E T
A ■ O ■ T E ■ L ■ S ■ A ■
R U M ■ C O N G E R E E L
D ■ E ■ H ■ I M ■ ■ K ■
Y E A R ■ W A T E R S K I
■ ■ B ■ S L ■ N ■ T ■ N
F R O S T Y ■ A C T I N G
I ■ U ■ R O ■ Y ■ P ■ ■
G E T R E A D Y ■ S P I T
H ■ ■ S ■ I S ■ L ■ R ■
T O A D S T O O L ■ I O U
E ■ P E ■ U ■ U ■ N ■ L
R A P I D ■ S C R A G G Y
```

234

```
■ A ■ A U ■ S S ■ S ■ T
D R A G O N ■ C A L L U P
■ M ■ H ■ L R ■ A ■ R ■
S O Y A ■ E N A B L I N G
■ U ■ S A ■ P ■ O ■ ■ ■
P R O T E S T ■ S M E L T
E ■ ■ ■ H O P ■ ■ O ■ ■
A D E P T ■ O U T L I V E
■ R ■ B ■ D O ■ E ■ ■ ■
S A V O U R E D ■ O U S T
V ■ M I ■ I K ■ I ■ ■ ■
T I E P I N ■ N U A N C E
■ D ■ T E ■ G ■ T ■ K ■
```

235

```
L O B E L I A ■ C A C T I
U ■ R ■ E P ■ R ■ U ■ N
R Y E ■ W H I T E N E S S
C ■ A D ■ A ■ E ■ U ■ ■
H A K E ■ P R O P O S A L
■ D ■ H Y ■ I C ■ A ■ ■
B O O H O O ■ I N D O O R
L ■ W U ■ P G ■ T ■ ■ ■
A M N E S I A C ■ A C H E
S ■ E Y ■ S H ■ E ■ ■ ■
T O W N S F O L K ■ E R R
E ■ E I ■ F I ■ G ■ I ■
D E B I T ■ F A T I G U E
```

236

```
P U M P I N G ■ P U M A S
O ■ U ■ D O ■ R ■ O U ■
P A D D L E S T E A M E R
U ■ D Y ■ L A E ■ G ■ ■
L I L T ■ C O M M E N C E
A ■ E A ■ W B ■ T ■ ■ ■
R O T U N D ■ A L M O N D
H ■ C R E ■ F R ■ ■ ■ ■
M U R D E R E R ■ S T Y E
E ■ O S ■ D T ■ R S ■ ■
C O U N T T H E H O U R S
C ■ G O ■ O E ■ T ■ U ■
A B H O R ■ T O Y S H O P
```

237

```
■ C ■ W ■ T M ■ S X ■ ■
H O R T I C U L T U R E ■
■ I E ■ M C ■ A A ■ ■ ■
G L A N C E ■ H A N D Y ■
■ D ■ Z ■ ■ ■ D ■ ■ ■ ■
B R I N G O U T ■ F U M E
E ■ E ■ N A O ■ I ■ ■ ■
G N A W ■ E N C I R C L E
■ B ■ ■ I ■ ■ D ■ ■ ■ ■
M E R G E ■ T H R O N E ■
O ■ O A ■ U I ■ E ■ ■ ■
A P R O N S T R I N G S ■
■ E ■ M ■ T N ■ D S ■ ■
```

238

```
■ C ■ S S ■ S F ■ F ■
G U L L E T ■ P U L L I N
■ C I ■ I E ■ E T ■ ■
S K I P ■ L E A V E O F F
■ O O ■ T R ■ C U ■ ■
C O I N B O X ■ C Y C L E
■ N N S ■ ■ ■ O ■ ■ ■
G E N I E ■ B U I L D U P
V ■ T ■ B N ■ E ■ N ■
D E T A I L E D ■ A L L Y
■ N L A I D ■ I ■ O ■
P L A I N S ■ A R E N A S
■ Y C ■ E L ■ N D ■ ■
```

339

Solutions

239

```
  S C   A Q   A S
S T I R U P   U N R O L L
  U   U   R   I   R   I
S C A N   I N F R I N G E
  C   C   C   F   V   H
B O Y H O O D   J E T T Y
      E   T   T   E
S E W E R   B U S L A N E
  L   N   G   C   O   A
W I L D D U C K   C I T Y
  X   E   I   B   A   I
W I Z A R D   O C T A V E
  R   R   E X   E   E
```

240

```
  C   F U   A I D   G   S
A G A I N S T   O V E R T
  S   W   E   R   N   A   I
H E N N A   I N S U R E R
  F     R   U       E
L I D   N A M E B A D G E
  O   U   E   I     U   N
W H E E D L I N G   P E T
  L       N   M     R
H O L D O F F   O P E R A
  A   I   A   E   N   V   I
R E S I T   S P E C I A L
  D   T   H A T   Y   L   S
```

241

```
M A R G I N A L I S E D
A   E   S   C   M X
S O R T O U T   P O P E
U   L   I   E   L   C
M A N I A   V O L C A N O
A       T   E   I   M
R O T T E R   T U R N I P
K   A   M   P     A
E M B R A C E   S O L A R
T   L   L   M   T I   I
  B E T A   B E A C O N S
  A   R   E   G   N   O
S U M M E R S E A S O N
```

242

```
B Y L A W   E X C I S E D
O   E   E   X   O   L   O
M I G R A T E   R E A C T
B   A   T   M   G   C
A I L   H O P P I C K E R
S   E   T   E     T   E
T H W A R T   C O G N A C
I   I   S   L     O
C O N T E N T E D   K E G
  E   P   R   T   H   N
T A B O O   O R I G A M I
O   A   C   N   M   K   S
W A R T H O G   E L I T E
```

243

```
K E Y I N   R E V I S I T
I   O   E   I   N   O
D A U N T E D   L O O S E
S   N   W   D   L   R
S A G   O I L T A N K E R
T   R   E     E   E
U P T A K E   G A R L I C
F   R   E D   D   I
F L A T T E N E D   A M P
  I   E   D I L   L   I
M I N I M   I N C L I N E
D   E   P   N   T   B   N
F U R L O N G   S A I N T
```

244

```
S C R I B E   F U S S
P   U   O   B   N   P   R
R U M B A   O F F S I D E
A   M   S O B   A   N   P
T R Y S T   B A Z O O K A
    E       Y   E   U   I
A F F E C T   E D I T O R
M   L   O   I   C
B O A T M A N   W E D G E
U   V   M   D O E   R   X
S T O R A G E   L L A M A
H   U   N   X   L   K   L
  R U D E   A S P E C T
```

245

```
C H A M P I O N   C U R B
O   D   A   C   C   P   R
C L A S S I C   L A P S E
O     S   U   A   E   A
A R O M A   P O W E R E D
    R   G   Y   C   T
P A D D E D   S H E A T H
A   E   P   O   S
R E R O U T E   P R E S S
A   F   R   R   E       I
P R O N G   S O F A B E D
E   R   E   O   U   O   L
T I M E   A N A L O G U E
```

Solutions

246

```
  C A   M   R T   S
Q U A R T O   E Q U I T Y
  P   D   L U G   N   R
M O M E N T   A N N U A L
  L   N   E   R   E   I
C A R T O N   D I L A T E
  O               L
R I B B E D   M E D L E Y
  N   I   O   A   E   S
E T H N I C   N O V I C E
  O   B   I O N   I   A
E N T A I L   E X C E P T
  E   G   E   D   E   E
```

247

```
W I R E D   S P O N S O R
O   E   E   H   W   C   U
R O A S T E R   N O O S E
K   C   E   E   U   R
E A T   N E W S P A P E R
T   T   D       I   E
H A C K E R   S M O O C H
I   O   C   E   E
C O N C E A L E D   B R A
  T   V   O   I   L   R
F L O R A   N U C L E U S
O   U   D E   A E   A
G A R T E R S   L A P E L
```

248

```
F U C H S I A   G I R L S
I   H   I   U   O   O   H
G U A R D O F H O N O U R
M   R   E   A   D   T   E
E M M Y   W I L D C A R D
N   B   D   T   E   N
T U R N I N   W A N D E R
A   A   C   L   B   U
O N C E M O R E   D R A B
F   E   O   O   A A   I
F I L I N G C A B I N E T
A   E   D   U L C   I
L O T U S   S A Y W H E N
```

249

```
  M   D W   L   D   A
A U R O R A   E V E N T S
  E   L   R I G   N   L
A S Y L U M   E X T R A S
  L   O   E   N   A   S
S I M P E R   D E L E T E
      O               O
K O W T O W   P U R S E R
  P   H   O   U   A   G
S T R I V E   R E N E G E
  O   N   F E E   K   N
K U N G F U   L O L L O P
  T   S   L   Y   E   G
```

250

```
T U B   V I D E O G A M E
Y   U   N   E   R L   Y
P I G M E N T   G R I M E
E   B C   A A   V   S
F L E C K   C O N V E X
A   A   H   Z       G
C U R T S Y   F A S C I A
E       A   A   E   L
  P R I M A L   F O R G O
G   I   U   K L   T   S
U N D E R   A B O L I S H
L   E   A L   O   F   E
F O R T I F I E D   Y E S
```

251

```
  S E N S A T I O N A L
H   Y   P A   A   D   E
O V E R A M B I T I O U S
O   O   C   L S   R S
P R E C E D E D   K N E E
S   X   B T   I   M   X
  D E C A Y   A M B E R
W   R   R B   P   N   P
H A C K   V I B R A T E S
I   I   L   N   I   A
C A S T I N G A S P E L L
H   E   S E   O   A   M
  A S S A S S I N A T E
```

252

```
C A P A C I T Y   L I N O
A   L   C   A S   D   L
R E A C T   U S H E R E D
E   Y   V G   E   I   H
R I O T   C H A R I S M A
    F   D T   B       N
R A F F I A   K E Y P A D
E   C   P   T   O
F R O N T I E R   B U S T
U   N A   A H   R   E
G L I S T E N   A L I E N
E   O   E U   V   N   T
E T N A   S T R E N G T H
```

Solutions

253

M	S		C	I		I		W	B
O	U	T	L	A	S	T	E	D	A	L	E
S		I		L		A		O	N		R
C	A	R	A	M	E	L		L	A	D	L	E
O			D		I			E			T
W	A	S		O	N	C	E	M	O	R	E
		P		W			O		E	
	L	E	O	N	A	R	D	O		D	U	D
M		C			E		N			O
U	N	T	I	L		T	O	B	Y	J	U	G
S		A		U		U		E		O		E
H	U	T		C	A	R	N	A	T	I	O	N
Y		E		Y		N		M		N		D

254

	A		S	U	E		I	I
D	E	C	I	S	I	V	E	N	E	S	S
O		U		E		E		C		P
F	R	A	M	E	D		R	A	L	L	Y
A		A			C			U
A	B	S	T	R	A	C	T		D	A	T	A
L		R		R		E		O
S	E	M	I		S	T	A	N	D	O	U	T
		A				C		R
	M	I	N	E	D		A	R	C	T	I	C
E		G	A			K		R		S
H	E	A	L	T	H	R	E	S	O	R	T
K		E		L		S		P		S

255

	E	A	T	I	N	G	A	P	P	L	E
D		B		M		L		A		O		P
I	N	C	O	M	P	A	N	Y	W	I	T	H
V			O		R		S		T		O
E	N	F	O	R	C	E	S		W	E	N	T
R		R		T		D		P		R		O
	B	Y	L	A	W		F	L	U	I	D
W		I		L		S		A		N		S
A	U	N	T		P	E	N	T	A	G	O	N
T		G		T		R		O			A
E	X	P	E	R	I	M	E	N	T	I	N	G
R		A		I		O		I		C		S
	U	N	C	O	N	N	E	C	T	E	D

256

S	T	R	U	T		P	I	R	A	N	H	A
P		A		W		I		U		O		I
I	N	V	O	I	C	E		S	E	W	E	R
N				N			S					B
A	M	N	E	S	I	A		I	M	A	G	E
L		G			S		A		N			D
	E	M	P	T	Y	H	A	N	D	E	D
G		A		E		E			L		L
A	D	D	L	E		S	P	L	O	D	G	E
R			N				O		O		S
L	L	A	M	A		V	A	C	A	T	E	S
I		L		G	A		U		E		O
C	H	I	M	E	I	N		M	A	S	O	N

257

	B	R	I	T	I	S	H		C	R	A	B
E		I		I		C		C		I		A
L	A	P		P	U	R	C	H	A	S	E	R
E		E		T		A		R		O		K
M	A	R	S	H		P	A	I	N	T	S
E			E			S		T		P
N	U	D	I	S	M		S	T	R	O	L	L
T		O		C		M		E
	B	R	E	A	S	T		A	T	S	E	A
H		M		L		R		S		T		S
A	L	I	C	E	B	A	N	D		A	G	E
L		C		S		W		A		T		D
F	E	E	D		P	L	A	Y	P	E	N

258

T	I	P	O	F	F		C	E	N	S	O	R
O		L		A		D		N		W		A
U	S	A		R	O	U	N	D	N	E	S	S
P		N		E		M		E		P
E	L	B	O	W		B	R	E	A	T	H	S
E			E			F		L		E
	A	T	A	L	O	O	S	E	E	N	D
		Y		L		U		V		G
C	R	I	M	S	O	N		E	N	T	R	Y
U		N		D		N		A		R
R	E	G	I	S	T	E	R	S		B	R	A
V			E		D		E		O		T
Y	I	P	P	E	E		A	S	H	O	R	E

259

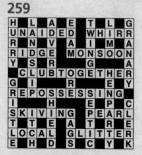

	H		L		A		E	T		L		G
U	N	A	I	D	E	D		W	H	I	R	R
R		N		V		A	I		M		R	A
R	I	D	G	E		M	O	N	S	O	O	N
Y		S		R			G			A		A
	C	L	U	B	T	O	G	E	T	H	E	R
G		I				E				Y
R	E	P	O	S	S	E	S	S	I	N	G
I			H			E		P		C
S	K	I	V	I	N	G		P	E	A	R	L
T		T		E		A		T		R		E
L	O	C	A	L		G	L	I	T	T	E	R
E		H		D		S		C		Y		K

Solutions

260

```
A . M . C . A . N . S . G
T E E T H . A D A P T O R
O . A . A . C . R . A . E
M O N A R C H . C U R S E
I . I . . . E . I . D . .
C O N F R O N T S . G U Y
. . G . . . E . . . S . .
A S S . H A I R I N E S S
R . . . E . . . A . . . A
G A M M A . D E P O S I T
E . I . R . I . O . I . I
N I C O S I A . O W N E R
T . E . E . N . L . G . E
```

261

```
O . M . R . E . S . O . D
B R A V E . M I N I B A R
L . E . E . O . E . Y . Y
O N O F F E R . B U Y E R
N . O . . . G . B . . . O
G O N O W H E R E . R A T
. . E . H . . . R . E . .
S A D . E N J O Y M E N T
C . . . N . O . . . N . U
U N C L E . R E C L A I M
R . U . V . D . O . C . B
V E R B E N A . M O T E L
Y . E . R . N . E . S . E
```

262

```
S . B . R . . . C . S . P
C A R E E R . T A M P E R
H . E . F . S . T . R . E
O M E L E T T E S . Y E T
O . D . R . B . . . T . .
L O I T E R E R S . F R Y
. . N . E . R . H . R . .
C O G . D U N G A R E E S
O . . . A . M . E . W . .
A D D . H O R S E S H O E
R . R . O . F . O . A . .
S T I G M A . C U T L E T
E . P . E . . . L . D . Y
```

263

```
F . L . S . R . E . F . B
O V E R H E A R D . L E A
R . T . O . I . I . Y . N
W A S T E R S . T E P I D
A . . . I . A . . . A . Y
R U B . W I N D P I P E .
D . A . H . . . A . E . W
. I G N O R A N T . R Y E
S . P . . . L . . . A . A
T W I N E . W O B B L E S
R . P . U . A . A . E . I
A T E . R O Y A L M A I L
P . R . O . S . D . N . .
```

264

```
N A S S A U . S A D D L E
. V . C . N . I . E . A .
P O L O . D E D I C A T E
. C . U . E . E . E . E .
P A S T U R E S . N O R M
. D . S . P . C . . . . .
R O C K E T . L A Y I N G
. E . A . I . . . O . . .
S T Y E . N A T I V I T Y
O . P . D . T . I . H . .
G R A F F I T I . P R I M
. S . I . N . N . E . N .
D O G T A G . G A R A G E
```

265

```
S T R O N G E R . D A F T
. I . N . R . O . A . L .
A N N E X E . T O Y B O Y
. S . E . S . P . S . P .
D E S C E N D S . C A P E
. L . L . H . T . H . Y .
. D E T O N A T O R . . .
W . R . R . R . O . S . .
B A N G . N O B I L I T Y
. S . Y . O . . . A . . .
T H A M E S . A S P I R E
U . A . K . R . E . V . .
S P A N . I N D A N G E R
```

266

```
S P U R . O V E R E A T S
. E . T . M . N . . . E .
S N I T C H . I N S A N E
. D . R . E . N . . . U .
C U T E . R E E L E C T S
. L . A . . . N . . . R .
M U L T I N A T I O N A L
. M . . . O . . . B . N .
A S T E R O I D . V E S T
. . . N . D . E . I . F .
H O S T E L . V I O L E T
. W . E . O . . . U . R .
I N P R I S O N . S O S O
```

Solutions

267

```
R A T R A C E   T W E E
B   G   E   R   S   R   V
E A R A C H E   K N I F E
L   E   O   E   I   T   N
G R E E N   P O T A T O
I   N   Y   T   E   S
A R G U E D   C L I N I C
N   O   C   P   E   A
  S U I T O R   A R S O N
A   R   I   I   L   T   D
R O M A N   S U L T A N A
C   E   G   O   E   I   L
H A T E   U N T Y I N G
```

268

```
N O T I C E   S T A P L E
E   O   D   R   A   E   N
S U B U R B S   N A S A L
T   A   O   P   T   T   I
  S C A M   C U R I O U S
S   C   A   U   U   T
P R O M P T   I M M U N E
E   I   C   N   D
  C R Y S T A L   D O L E
I   O   I   A   E   O   L
F L U F F   S U M M A R Y
I   R   U   S   O   D   N
C O S T L Y   U N I S E X
```

269

```
  A D V A N C E   A L E C
T   O   M   H   A   E   O
Y U C C A   A R S E N I C
R   S   S   S   G   K
R A R T I S T E   I O T A
N   R   D   G   H   G
T R A S H Y   U N V E I L
S   U   U   A   N   A
  A M E N   C H A S S I S
P   A   G   I   D   G
U T T E R E D   D I S C O
M   I   Y   I   O   W
P A C T   E C O N O M Y
```

270

```
  B   N   B D W   S
C R E O S O T E   E A C H
  E   W   R   L   P   R
S A L A M I   E X T R A
  C   D   N   T   W
S H I A   G R E E N F L Y
  Y       E
I C E S K A T E   C O S H
  O   C   N   K   I
  W I P E R   G A T H E R
  B   I   O   A   I   S
H O R N   S E G M E N T S
  Y   K   S   E   S   A
```

271

```
  T   P   U U   R   I
O U T L I N E S   U R G E
  N   I   C   E   I   N
C A N A D A   R A N D O M
  N   N   N   E   R
E D I T I N G   A D L I B
  O   Y   N   N   N
I N E P T   C O N S I G N
  A   U   W   O
E T H N I C   H O R R O R
  I   I   A   E   B   I
M O S S   S U R G E O N S
  N   H   K   E   T   K
```

272

```
C I N E M A   H O L M E S
O   U   A   P   I   I
B A C O N   O V E R A W E
W   L   I   P   R   O   N
E L E G A N T   A R W E N
B   U   I   T   A
  S P O O N F E E D
A   N   G   I   E
B U G L E   O N B O A R D
A   R   T   U   R   L   W
C H A R I O T   A R E N A
U   D   M   V   C
S W E D E N   P O S T E D
```

273

```
I N T E A R S   B A S I C
N   O   W   H   O   U   U
S A L S A   O C T O B E R
I   E   K   D   H   S   L
G O T R E A D Y   K I S S
H   N   Y   P   D
T U R R E T   O R D E A L
  U   D   R   E   I
T R I M   S A U C E P A N
I   N   G   I   E   L   E
R E I G N E D   D R E A D
E   N   A   E   E   A   U
D I G I T   D E S K T O P
```

Solutions

274

```
G E T A L S
CONFIRMS ETCH
W F U I T A
UNLOAD ASSENT
R G G T
UMPTEEN TOXIC
A S G L
SCUBA VALLEYS
K U L I
CENSUS LONELY
R T A A K I
SEAL LANGUISH
L E E T P P
```

275

```
OSTRICH BATH
D A E O O O
OLIVE LASAGNE
Z L L L I G
ELBA DISTRESS
D O D E C L
SAVED NOVEL
R G G M C S
UNDERWAY STEP
O E T I I R
PRECEDE NOOSE
T O A C N E
WHEN DUCHESS
```

276

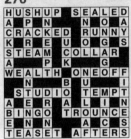

```
HUSHUP SEALED
A P N N O A
CRACKED RUNNY
K R E U G S
STEAM COLLAR
A P K G
WEALTH ONEOFF
N B U I
STUDIO TEMPT
A E R A L I N
BINGO TROUNCE
E N N A C S
TEASET AFTERS
```

277

```
THISTLE ODDS
R Y L I O L
EYESORE RADIO
M N T L A D P
ALARM OUTSET
T A W T R P
CRUTCH PLAYER
H N H L E E
ESKIMO STUNT
H O N O N R E
AMUSE SOAPBOX
I N E K A T
LADY INFERNO
```

278

```
O C A FICO
BRASSBAND OFF
L N S S E M F
INEXACT APPLE
G S E R R
EYE STRAINED
D I M S
RUNNERUP SAW
G C E O A
REALM DELUDED
O T O I I A E
ACE PLASTERER
N D E L E N S
```

279

```
SAUSAGEROLL
B R Q R E E G
ONCEUPONATIME
R A C R C E
EMBARKED NESS
D R E R L S E
JOLLY DEATH
G W Y P O E S
LONG CORPORAL
O B S P A A
BREATHEFREELY
E A A Y D G S
PROGRESSION
```

280

```
PUBLICAN HARK
A U C M G B I
RIFLE ACROBAT
I F D Z I O C
SOAK TOPNOTCH
L C N D E
SPOTON PERSON
U N H R H
BEAUTIES LOCH
S R A L A W O
IDOLISE BAMBI
D M N N L E S
YEAR HAZELNUT
```

Solutions

281

```
S E O W H C A
A R G Y B A R G Y   U R N
D   G   J   I   M   R G
D I S S E N T   N E R V E
E   C   E       E   E L
N I L   T O R C H I N G
    E   O       Y   T
  S M A R T E N S   S O B
H   O   S   T       R
A N N U L   C H E L S E A
R   A   O   O   R   I N
D A D   A I R L I F T E D
Y   E   F   T   A   E Y
```

282

```
A   D   G   C   M   C
S T E E R C L E A R O F
C   A   A   U   R   I
B E R L I N   B E G A N
N   N       I
O D D I T I E S   N A P E
E   C   N   O   A   O
E D G E   G A M B L E R S
L       E       T
S T O O L   W A T E R Y
T   L   E   H   E   A
B O W L I N G A L L E Y
P   Y   T   T   L   S
```

283

```
  C O M P A C T D I S C
G   B   L   L   R   P S
R E E X A M I N A T I O N
O   Y   E   G   N   O
W A F F L I N G   T S A R
S   O   I   T   F   T T
  C R U S T   R I V E T
R   B   T   L   R   R F
U N I T   W A T E R S K I
M   D   F   P   A   G
M U D D L E T H R O U G H
Y   E   E   O   M   S T
  U N D E R P A S S E S
```

284

```
E L D E R   R E L E A S E
I   E   A   E   I   R X
G O T O B E D   T W E E T
H   E   B       E   O
T U R K I S H   R I P E R
H   G   O   A   R   T
  T E E T O T A L L E R
C   N   A   E   S   O
L A T E X   L E C T E R N
U   I   O   R   E
T O N I C   B E L O V E D
C   A   A   I   I E A
H A N D B A G   C A D D Y
```

285

```
  P R I V A T E   M O A N
W   O   I   I   A   R O
R A W   C O M P L A I N S
E   E   T   E   L   G H
C A R L O   S L O G A N
K   R   F   M   D
E Y E L I D   M A L I C E
D   N   A   S   F
  S H A P E D   U T T E R
L   A   L   E   D   A O
A N N O U N C E D   B U S
M   C   M   O   E   L T
B E E P   G R I N N E D
```

286

```
S E S A M E   L O I T E R
H   O   I   H   W   O O
R A F   N O I S E L E S S
E   I   E   G   N   I
W E A N S   H E C T A R E
D   H   P   O   I
  I M P A T I E N T L Y
A   F   T   D   A
F A N A T I C   E M A I L
A   M   H   N   B   B
S E A F A R E R S   O R E
T   D   L   D   E V R
S T E V I E   A D V E R T
```

287

```
S   C   W   O   H   P U
C E I L I N G   U N I O N
I   V   S   R   M   E G
F R I E D   E M B A R G O
I   L   O   U       D
  S W I M M I N G P O O L
S   A   C   P   Y
C A R B O H Y D R A T E
U   U   E   I   E
F R A N T I C   A C O R N
F   G   I   U   S   N D
L I E I N   F O O T A G E
E   S   G   F   N   L D
```

Solutions

288

```
U A T   P U B S
SOPPY   REMNANT
E   P R E B B R
FORCEPS   RHYME
U   O   T E   A
LIVERPOOL   ARM
    E   E L V
ROD   THERAPIST
E   A   X   A I
CACTI   PITSTOP
O   A L O R I O
ILLNESS   ALOOF
L   L R E M N F
```

289

```
A   G S P   S W D
SNARL   IMITATE
Y   N A G   M N P
LEGIBLE   PATIO
U   E   O L   R
MADESENSE   LOT
  U   C     S O
SAP   AUDITIONS
M     N E     P E
URGED   MUGSHOT
D   R A A   I O T
GREMLIN   FALSE
E   Y S D T   E R
```

290

```
S   F D   N P M
TILTED   DEFUSE
A   Y R L   W R L
RESTRAINT   RAT
E   P   I M   E
DIRTCHEAP   ODD
  A K   J R P
SAY   SOUWESTER
T     I D   I I
REF   RECLAIMED
O   A A E   T I I
BIKINI   POISON
E E G   R T G
```

291

```
I   B A J E   W S
CROSSWORD   EAT A
E   O K S   G A A
BABYSIT   YOKEL
E     L   E E K
RIG   SPEEDING
G   U   U E G
  UNDERFED   DRY
R   M   I     M
ONAIR   LETDOWN
U   K O T   I V A
TEE   ACHIEVERS
E R M Y R N T
```

292

```
ITALIC   DANISH
  A A H A O M
SPRY   REDEEMED
  I E   I D N L
TOURISTY   TILL
  C   T   L R
SAFARI   OXYGEN
  U   A N   L
AGED   NIGHTIES
R   I   N L A V
MORTGAGE   STAR
O   O M   G T T
EMERGE   STEREO
```

293

```
PEEKABOO   PUFF
  N I A   I R A
SCENIC   KEEPUP
  O   K   M L
CROCUSES   ACTS
  E A L W T Y
    AMBITIOUS
  L E D N R A
PAIR   EGGHEADS
  G A   B   J
GOSSIP   ONFOOT
  O H T A R I
ENVY   OUTLYING
```

294

```
WORM   STRAPPED
  B U W E R L
LEAGUE   SPOOKY
  D T L P B
LIAR   LOITERED
  E E   T N
UNDERTHEKNIFE
  C   R E O
SEDATING   TURF
  L C U B C
ATRISK   ARABIA
  O C E R L N
INTENDED   LOGO
```

Solutions

295

```
  T O A S T E R   U S E D
S   N   P   N   W   T   U
U N T W I S T   O N I O N
M   A   N   I   O   M   K
M A P L E   C A L L U S
O   C   E   G   L     W
N O U G H T   C A L I C O
S   S   I   T   T     R
  C U R L E R   H U M I D
A   A   L   I   E   U   I
M E L E E   F O R E S E E
O   L   R   L   E   I   R
K E Y S   V E R R U C A
```

296

```
E N D U R E   G L O B A L
M   R   E   I   L   I
I R E L A N D   B L O C K
T   D   D   I   E   O   E
  U G L Y   O A R S M A N
P   E   M   A       I
A R R E S T   S L I P O N
M     E   F     O   G
P A S S A G E   V O T E
H   C   W   V   I   T   T
L L A M A   E X T R E M E
E   L   L   R   A   R   N
T O P P L E   P L A Y E D
```

297

```
  E S C A P E D   D R A B
C   K   R   N O   E   O
O P I U M   C A L Y P S O
M   E   O   D   R   M
P R O D D E D   E P I C
O   V   E   S   N   W
S T E N C H   S T I T C H
E   R   A   P   E   E
  S C A N   R E S I D U E
F   R   N   A   T   L
E C O L O G Y   A L I B I
E   W   N   E   C C   E
T I D E   T R E K K E D
```

298

```
  D   S   F   A   C C
D E L I V E R S   H A L E
  C   M   L   S   I   E
P E N P A L   U L C E R
  I   E   O   R   G
S T I R   W E E K D A Y S
  E           A
D E A D E N E D   R E E K
  X   U   I   K   L
T U N E D   N A R R O W
  R   I   I   G   O   P
B A I L   S C H O O L E D
  S   E   T   Y   M   D
```

299

```
  F   S   C   A   Q   A
B A C K C H A T   U N D O
  I   I   E   O   A   M
C R I N G E   M I R R O R
  N   R       R   N
A C R Y L I C   C Y N I C
  O   O   U       S
C H A O S   S T A R C H Y
  E   P   I   E
A S S E S S   L A W Y E R
  I   N   P   A   A
R O B E   A S T E R I S K
  N   D   R   Y   D   T
```

300

```
M A K E U P   E I T H E R
E   E   N   S   A   I
A G E N T   D R O P L E T
G   P   I   L   V   U
R O M P E R S   A K E L A
E   U   A   T   L
  M E A N S T E S T   S
V   I   T   S   S   S
E X C E L   E X H A U S T
L   A   M   R   O   N   U
V A L U E R S   P S A L M
E   V   N   I   M   P
T R E A T Y   S T A I R S
```